# STAG AT BAY

# STAG AT BAY
## *The Scottish Red Deer Crisis*

MICHAEL WIGAN

SWAN·HILL
PRESS

Copyright © 1993 by Michael Wigan

First published in the UK in 1993
by Swan Hill Press an imprint of Airlife Publishing Ltd

**British Library Cataloguing in Publication Data**
A catalogue record for this book
is available from the British Library

ISBN 1 85310 457 4

Printed by Livesey Ltd, Shrewsbury

Swan Hill Press
an imprint of Airlife Publishing Ltd
101 Longden Road, Shrewsbury SY3 9EB

# Contents

'Every population of animals exists in a highly dynamic state, growing in size if it can, thrusting into new terrain when permitted, evolving in new directions as opportunity arises.'

*The Diversity of Life*

Edward O. Wilson, 1992

# Preface

Many people have contributed to this book, some in ways they will never know. The reactions of people to being in proximity to wild deer have always interested me, and I have put mental markers down on many throwaway thoughts and comments. Principally though, I would like to thank those who have been of direct help on the subject of the red deer today. These, in no special order, are: Ronnie Rose, Patrick Gordon-Duff-Pennington, Dick Youngson, Brian Staines, Des Thompson, Alistair Strathnaver, Colin McKelvie, John Grant, Hugh Rose, Colin Shedden, Kerry Keysell, Peter Swales, Dick Balharry, Louis Stewart, Niall Graham-Campbell, Jamie Williamson, Tim Clutton-Brock, Jonathan Mason, John Lister-Kaye, Neil Ramsay, Colin Gibb, David Laird and Roger Wadsworth.

Stalkers over the years on different estates have helped me form the picture of red deer on which any under-standing I have is based. In particular I would like to pay tribute for their great deer knowledge and hill sense to Donald Geddes, with whom I stalked my first stag when I was thirteen and who is now performing the same service with my son, Albert Grant, Terry Rowantree, John MacLennan and Geordie Oswald.

The books I have used for reference have been *Red Deer In The Highlands* and *Red Deer: Behaviour and Ecology Of Two Sexes*, both by Tim Clutton-Brook and Steve Albon, the latter also having Fiona Guinness as

1

co-author; *A Herd of Red Deer* by Frank Fraser Darling; *The Natural History of Deer* by Rory Putnam; and *Monarchs Of The Glen* by Duff Hart-Davis. Tim Clutton-Brook has been studying red deer for twenty-five years and most of the second chapter is based on his and his associates' findings. This work would not have been possible without the co-operation of Cambridge University and government funding from the Natural Environment Research Council and the Science and Engineering Research Council. Much of the research was done on the island of Rhum with the leave of the former Nature Conservancy Council and, more recently, Scottish Natural Heritage.

# Chapter 1

I live on a deer forest. My home is at Borrobol, a remote place in central east Sutherland, and the far end of the Borrobol Forest is one of the furthest places from a public road on the map of Britain. The principal inhabitants of this patch of flow country peatland are red deer, and although the identifiable ancestors of our own red deer were present ten million years ago, the existing genetic strain have probably been in occupation here for some 20,000 years. For reasons of politeness alone it therefore behoves me to have good regard for these ancient locals.

For they are the neighbours. During most of the fifteen years I have been here I have lived alone, along with the three other resident households. In solitary circumstances the wildlife around makes an impact on one's mind and penetrates one's imagination in a way which is hard to understand without having been experienced. When a roaring stag is making guttural grunts behind the garden fence as one drifts off to sleep, it is hard not to ponder on the private lives of the neighbours who are no less companionable for being covered in rough hair and walking on four legs. In storm times I thought of them compassionately, having, from time to time, to stay on the hill in just those conditions, when in the business of regulating their numbers. Despite the many obvious differences, the feeling I describe is the same in type to that of a shepherd for his flock. Moreover, I get a simple pleasure in watching the deer as they go their diurnal rounds, observing them eating, running, dozing, gazing steadily with infinitely alert intelligence at whatever has arrested their attention. Despite being a keen stalker I have frequently drifted off, sprawled on some heathery knoll whilst waiting to fire the shot, in happy contemplation of their activities. It is impossible to imagine ever getting bored of them, or becoming indifferent to their grace and beauty.

They have always seemed a permanent feature of the Borrobol landscape. This permanence overrides the generations in subtle ways. Six or so years back two remarkable stags attracted my attention after the stag groups had reassembled following the rut. One had a wonderful classic head, a perfectly balanced 'royal', or stag with twelve points on his antlers. The tops of his crown antlers were long, and strayed out like the branch-tops of ancient trees, in a way stalkers describe as truly wild, belonging only to a true hill stag. His body was thick and deep and long and his colour russet. Always close by him stayed another stag, a marginally larger animal and with an extraordinary head, very tall, enormously thick in the horn, and parading thirteen points. They held each other's company, aloof from the rest of the seventy-odd party, and I believed on the basis of their abnormal size and the similar shape of the face and nose that they might have been half-brothers. I photographed them once in perfect conditions against a snowscape backlit by the falling winter sun. The years passed and then one day in 1992, again after the rut I was watching the 'feeder' stags on the self-same hill when I noticed what appeared to be the familiar pair, vividly preserved in my mind by the photograph. They too held a little aloof; I could almost have repeated the original photograph. Yet, of course, they were different animals, the other two, each at least twelve at the time, having long ago passed on. I was surely beholding their descendants, curiously paired

4

together again. Biologically there is, naturally, nothing remarkable in this. Genetically-related red deer occupy traditionally-held territories, the hinds holding them throughout most of the year, the stags ranging somewhat further. Physical characteristics pass down the line in deer as in other mammals. The point is that this image from the past, for me, highlighted their permanence.

Their permanence is, however, a delusion. In the world of the late twentieth century there are virtually no populations of big mammals anywhere which have not been tampered with by man. Even the great caribou herds in the last wildernesses of Canada have been substantially altered by man's activities. Europe is a crowded place and it is hardly surprising that its largest land-based denizen needs to squeeze into the corners and crevices to survive. Indeed, in most of Europe the red deer have declined or disappeared over the centuries. Only in Scotland, on open hills and moors, is the population large enough, and in sufficiently suitable surroundings, to offer to viewers the 'plains experience' of watching large animals moving in herds over the open landscape in a tolerable imitation of primaeval freedom. Strange though it may seem there is now a powerful movement afoot to change this, a body of opinion which believes, or purports to believe, that this spectacle is proof, not of our success in preserving a magnificent part of our wildlife heritage, but of an insufficiently controlled population. And for several years now every media organization with pretences to wildlife and environment awareness has broadcast stories about the red deer's population problem, and the environmental danger posed by this.

Broadcast is the correct word; for on many occasions the accusations made against deer have been wide of the mark. Generalizations about deer numbers have been made on the basis of population problems in localized areas. Some of the remedies that have been proposed for the 'red deer crisis' have also shown that deer are being used by social reformers, privately interested in altering land ownership patterns and making anachronistic the term 'deer forest', under the guise of environmentalism. Thus it is that the animal once christened by the Victorian artist Sir Edwin Landseer 'The Monarch of the Glen' is now being called vermin, a depiction which frankly bemuses many of those for whom the stag has become one of the popular insignia of Scotland. How has this reversal of reputation occurred? Somewhere along the line have we failed properly to assess wildlife values? Is the theory of reduced habitat, and moorland degradation, being used as a pretext for treating the famously vexed matter of land-ownership in Scotland? Wildlife management cannot be separated from habitat management, and must pursue long-term, worked-out objectivism not faddish whimsicalities. In this book I want to look at Scottish red deer, to try to clear the air of the more misleading interpretations, and see what future there is for this big mammal which arouses such strong feelings.

Our approach to deer is at a crossroads. The deer question impinges on many disputes of the day, about land use, land-ownership, access to wild land and the conservation of our few remaining wild areas. There is a danger that the deer themselves are becoming a pawn in a good, old-fashioned struggle for control, control of the Scottish hills. The disadvantages of my perspective as a landowner with vested interests may hopefully be outweighed by the advantages of a commentary coming from one with an economic interest in deer, which demands sustainable management of land, and with an equal interest, both economic and temperamental, in varied wildlife and habitat. Land use as a whole fascinates me, but my favourite activity is stalking, and my favourite purpose is the regeneration of old woodlands. I would also like to think that the views I express are not mine alone, but have developed by talking with those concerned with the practical management of deer, such as stalkers, those visitors who come here to look at deer, and those for whom also, the red deer are the neighbours.

# Chapter 2

It is no accident that the red deer was the animal chosen by mediaeval royalty as being expressly their own hunting quarry. Anyone else hunted the stag on pain of death. Even on the hunting preserves awarded to the nobility the stag was still the monarch's own; his feudal vassals had to make do with fallow deer, foxes, and 'beasts of the chase'. For the stag has about it something regal, in its prancing walk, and its mighty antlered head, upon which the monarch's own crown is based.

Science has followed our feelings of reverent curiosity and now the red deer is the biologically best understood mammal in Britain. What do we know? One of the interesting recent discoveries is that deer change their pelage seasonally. The summer coat which has no underwool is replaced in winter by a longer pelt below which a thick underwool develops between September and December. Deer moult back into summer vestments in late April and May, older animals and yeld (barren) hinds changing first. Calves moult twice in their first year, when the spots fade from their coats two months after birth, and prior to winter.

Red deer have developed long limbs and strong muscles, and highly acute sense organs, to compensate for the fact that they cannot fend off large predators; survival chances depend on rapid awareness of possible danger, and then the means of getting sharply away. Another adaptation is related to their herbivorous diet.

They are cud-chewers with a complex four-chambered stomach. When first bitten off, food is ingested into the first stomach chamber and stored. Deer watchers will recall being surprised initially at the incessant fast grazing that crams vegetation into the stomach as quickly as possible. Feeding so intently puts them at risk from predation. So when the rumen chamber is full they retire to a safe place to regurgitate the indigestible plant material. Meanwhile the cellulose-digesting micro-organisms have begun work on the food, breaking its woody matter down. Food is regurgitated and re-swallowed many times before it is passed down the line to the next treatment chamber, the reticulum. Further breakdown of the cellulose occurs here before the progressively reduced material goes into the intestine, passing through the remaining two stomach chambers *en route*. Thus red deer utilise low-grade plant material in a manner which minimizes their exposure to physical danger.

Hinds and stags are now known to have differing diets. Obviously diet opportunities vary from place to place in Scotland, the availability of seaweed, for example, only being open to coastal deer. In general terms, however, hinds monopolize the better feeding areas, with superior base minerals, particularly in winter, and eat more grass than stags and less heather. Stags, which have bigger bodies, and therefore bigger rumens in which to break down hard plants, are able to equal the amount of nitrogen in their system as hinds, despite consuming the less nutritious heather. For larger-bodied animals can tolerate poorer-quality foods. Stags graze more at night than hinds, and invariably on lower-quality pasture. Some theorists now believe that the differing diet is part of the explanation for red deer's sexual segregation. For, the rut aside, Scottish stags and hinds live mostly apart. Only in the rut are they together, the stags coming from their summer grazings at the end of September to carve out for themselves a harem of hinds. The rutting territories are small but indefatigably worked, the stag challenging all comers and completely absorbed in the task of defending his harem. Normally the stag works his hinds downhill, while their stravaigings take them uphill. As fresh stags enter the arena to challenge, and spent or beaten stags retire, the rutting territories become more elastic.

The ecologist Frank Fraser Darling believed that in red deer the grazing herd had reached its highest degree of social development; also that the persistence of the species, in the Scottish context, depended on it. Early studies of red deer behaviour in the wild started with him, and since his study of deer on the bleak Torridonian sandstone of Wester Ross, entitled *A Herd of Red Deer* and published in 1937, a legacy of considerable work has been done on the social grouping among Scottish red deer, and many fascinating insights have been gained. It is now clear, for example, that almost invariably small groups of hinds are family parties. This confirms what stalkers have often noted: that the faces of hinds in the same small group resemble each other. That these hinds occupy sharply-delineated territories is also proven, moving within them on the dictates of wind and weather and feeding, but basically remaining for their lives on home ground. Fraser Darling argued that, although sometimes in small groups, hinds belonged to widerspread matriarchies, which could cover an area of two square miles or so. On islands I suspect this territory tends to be smaller than on the plains of the northern Highlands where geographical scale determines that territories are expansive. Islands tend to offer more variegated pasture and better shelter within smaller areas. As hind groups increase in size their reproductive success falls off. Within the groups large hinds can exert a considerable degree of dominance and push feebler animals off preferred pastures. Stags tend to congregate together in groups of similar ages, and scientists have noted more easy-going relationships between stags, excepting the rut of course, and generally more flexible group structures.

This scientific work supports the experience of those engaged in deer stalking. Stags typically charge off pell-mell after the shot, in no apparent formation. Each individual stag looks after himself primarily. This selfishness is most marked in very old stags, feeling the pinch of the years. They are prone to disassociating themselves from the group, retreating into corners to grumble away their remaining existences, moving in ever-decreasing circles. Hinds are quite different, and hind groups preserve their matriarchal structures when organizing a retreat. When stalking a party of mixed stags and hinds it is a hind, generally a large matriarch in good condition, that selects the escape route. Stags during the hind-shooting season, the dates of which they seem to have firmly fixed in their minds, lumber off half-heartedly in the wake of their female fellows, if they can be bothered to move fast at all. Whilst it has been shown that stags suffer winter less well than hinds, enduring greater heat loss, no physical explanation can satisfy, to me, the well-attested reality; stags know full well that hinds being picked off in a mixed party are no concern of theirs, and that showing a clean pair of heels as they follow the hinds is all a tiresome token performance.

A further area of investigation now illumined by researchers is the difference for hinds of bearing stag and hind calves. Stag calves are more costly in effort for hinds to produce, and hinds which have laboured to succour their more demanding male progeny are less likely to be fertile the following breeding season. Male calves are born heavier than females and the gestation period is a day or two longer. Male calves suckle longer, and the greater demands of stag calves are illustrated by the considerably later date at which hinds that have just raised a young stag calve in the following year. More male calves survive their first year, which it is presumed bio-logically compensates for the shorter lives of stags, and their greater susceptibility to winter mortality. Stags are understood to put more of their growing energy into simple physical growth than hinds, which pack more of their fodder into fat reserves to sustain them in winter.

Scientific study of stags has tended to show that the old traditions stalkers have been following in recent years, of weeding out stags 'going back', or passing their prime, has been broadly right. 'Master' stags which can hold a harem of hinds are capable of maintaining dominance for little longer than four years. Reproductive success is greater, on average, amongst hinds than stags, and many inferior stags never produce offspring at all. Work on Rhum suggested that as many as forty per cent of stags died without issue. Although it is not fully clear how many descendants a master stag can leave, and final resolution of this probably lies with future genetic science, it has been shown that dominant stags can leave at least twenty-five descendants which attain the age of one year (calf mortality in the wild is often around thirty per cent). More recent work using DNA fingerprinting indicates the figure could even be twice that. Most calves are conceived in October and there is a surprising synchronicity in the short period during which all stags are most potent. Whereas the breeding power of stags falls sharply off after age ten, for hinds the decline occurs later, after twelve years, and is markedly less pronounced. It has often been remarked in the deer larder, when weighing and sizing up the condition of deer culled in the hind season, that a particular old hind had a surprisingly good calf. Now it is proven that old hinds suckle their calves longer and produce calves more likely to survive the winter. Therefore the value of old hinds as producers falls off even less than their calving rate suggests. The traditional policy of shooting off yeld hinds rather than milkers, assuming the cull policy is for maximum sustainable yields of deer, is supported by findings that show the calves of yeld hinds suckling less than those of milkers, and surviving winters less well also. The explanation for this is that the factors which acted against a hind producing a calf once, such as poor physique, would do so again.

The present-day deer debate has centred on deer populations, and conservationists have expressed particular concern about top-heavy populations resulting in poorer habitat. Therefore the part of modern deer research which has the keenest and most direct interest for deer managers is connected with deer density, and the mechanics of population growth and contraction. The scientists have conspired to show that not only is the red deer an extraordinarily adaptive mammal, ranging over different habitats from Manchuria to North America, but its ability to regulate its own numbers is elaborate. The science of deer population growth is complex, but increased professionalism in the management of deer will entail trying to understand it. Much of it has been understood at the practical rather than theoretical level by the cannier stalkers of the past. It is a happy coincidence that exhaustive researches on Scottish deer have been published at the same time as deer management has become a headline topic.

The performance of stags, in condition and density, appears to be strongly determined by hind densities, so the key factor population researches needed to examine was reproduction by hinds. As with most mammals there is a close relationship between hind numbers and their fecundity. Hinds breed later in life when populations are high. On one hand pregnancy has occurred amongst calves within commercial forestry blocks; conversely hinds on open moorland breed as three-year-olds in high density populations. The former Nature Conservancy's experiments on the west coast of Rhum showed that the proportion of hinds that conceived as two-year-olds fell from 65 per cent to 10 per cent as densities increased. The rising densities affected some hinds more than others. No effects were observed on adult yeld hinds, but strong effects were seen on milk hinds. Milk hinds calving fell from 90 per cent to 30 per cent as numbers rose. The fecundity of three-year-olds fell from 70 per cent to 10 per cent. Similarly dramatic results have been shown on the mainland. It is known that fecundity is related closely to body weight. But comparing hind weights across the Scottish deer range can confuse the issue since body size varies widely. Furthermore wild hinds have never been systematically weighed, except when the breath is out of them, in deer larders. Population density also affected the time at which calves were born, high populations pushing calving times back. This in turn reduced their chances of survival, as they were smaller and weaker at the onset of winter.

Trying to separate the causes of natural mortality in deer was a problem for the Rhum scientists. However it appears that in unculled populations, or the natural state, calf mortality is more important in regulating population growth than adult death. Calves did not die straight after birth, but in autumn. As population densities rose the Rhum scientists came up with the striking figure for rising calf deaths in winter of less than 5 per cent to nearly 40 per cent. Yearling mortality also rose, from zero to 30 per cent. These figures were validated by those from that part of the island where populations were steady and culls were being carried out by stalking. Here calf numbers in their first spring remained constant. Of the factors affecting population increase it was calculated that increased mortality of calves was a stronger factor than either the falling fecundity of hinds, or adult deaths. In common with the biology of many other mammals pressures on individual survival brought on by population density principally affected males. On Rhum the proportion of males dying within their first two years rose from 10 per cent to 60 per cent, whilst for young females the figure rose from 10 per cent to 30 per cent. In young stags antler development was noticeably slowed down as populations grew. Whilst these figures are useful for Scottish deer managers it should be remembered that they are derived from a relatively stable situation on traditional deer range. What mechanisms apply when there is a complete population collapse is unknown, although it might be guessed at. A reindeer herd was introduced to St Matthew Island in the Bering Sea to succour American coastguards stationed there. The population boomed over twenty years and peaked at 6000. The following winter abetted the increasingly stressed supply of the natural food – lichens – to bring off a spectacular population collapse; by spring the herd was forty-two animals only. The most startling population increases that have been statistically recorded for Scottish reds have been in forestry. Here the proportion of adult hinds pregnant ranged from 40 per cent to over 90 per cent, and yearling pregnancies could move from zero to over 90 per cent. The fastest population rise in the last thirty years has not been on the traditional red deer range in Scotland, but in the new areas deer have colonized.

One of the factors which Scottish researchers have had to accommodate is that infinitely complicated matter – weather. Population movements could not be scientifically assessed regardless of environmental changes, and weather is one that is, with tolerable precision, measurable. Weather conditions vary hugely over the Scottish hills and hard rain is capable of falling in one glen when the next one along is bone-dry. Whether east and west coast deer populations have evolved to cope with their differing climates is unknown, apart from the obvious difference of body sizes. Stalkers know what the most punishing conditions on the hill are – low temperatures, strong winds and strong rain. Body heat saps quickly away. Deer recognize these dangers and are extremely adept at finding cover, of the right type in advance of bad weather. Recently I fenced off a brae of bog-willows for regeneration. Deer had been prone to snuggle into them in hard times. In the snow-storms of January 1993 they returned again to utilise a tiny kinked corner of the fence-line which gave complete shelter for a line of animals strung out behind it.

Hard winters have an obvious effect on stags which are prone to range further for winter sustenance having, as already described, been relegated to less nutritious winter range by the hinds. After cold, prolonged winters stags cast their antlers later, and weigh less the following autumn. Not only is there a clear relationship between the number of days with lying snow and adult mortality the following spring, but snowier winters accompanied by severe wind-chill factors are suspected of accentuating stag deaths a whole year later.

Climatic variation affects deer directly, but also by changing the quantity and quality of food. Low autumn temperatures cut short grass growth, and severe winter frosts can 'brown' heather shoots, delaying their growth in spring. Low spring temperatures delay the arrival of grass and, as all shepherds know, reduce the quality of milk on mothers, or dry them up altogether. Rain, which suits grass but not so much heather, may increase growth but it reduces the nutrients in the leaves. Waterlogged soils retard grass growth. Heather growth, which determines the winter food supply, is best in warm dry summers. Dry cold and deep snow need not be a bad thing as the snow-cover protects the heather from wind, but this is assuming the deer have somewhere else to go. Where wintering ranges have been planted with forestry, and fence-lines prevent the animals from getting lower down the hill to cover, fatalities can be numerous. The birth weights of calves have been shown to relate closely to temperatures in the spring, and underweight calves turn into substandard hinds, which in turn breed less well. Calves survival itself is closely related to weight at birth.

The Rhum scientists concluded their studies on weather and population by saying that natural mortality will never be entirely eliminated by hard culling by stalkers. Recent winters have led deer managers to conclude that even heavily culled populations will not always affect the proportional number of winter deaths. This is a significant fact, and has a bearing on the argument that deer should be culled to lessen their winter suffering. It was observed that during the winter of 1989–90, when there was appalling mortality in the western Highlands, numbers of deer were actually low, and death was caused by incessant cold and lashing rain bringing on pneumonia. Additionally, deer paid the price of being fenced off by forestry from low-ground wintering, and were trapped on fence-lines ringing higher ground.

The debate about commercial forestry in relation to deer has evolved through several stages. Deer managers from the outset disliked forestry plantations because they tended to select ground suited to deer in winter, and removed land from sporting use. We are now at the stage of the afforested area having, at any rate for the moment, ceased to expand substantially. Some 15 per cent of Scotland is under conifers. From the deer viewpoint this is an irreversible fact. It leads to the question of how this affects deer management, both inside the forestry fence and outside it. With such a large part of former deer range under an umbrella of pine needles the researches on deer in forestry have an invaluable significance. Great strides have been made and it has transpired that forestry and adjacent deer forest must for practical and effective management be regarded as a single unified area. Discoveries about deer behaviour in forestry not only provide information on which to base management decisions, but they tell us something about the vigour and adaptability of the red deer which helps in understanding their open-hill lives.

By making counts from high seats at dawn and dusk, and analysing pellet densities, researchers have found that deer are sometimes present at densities of up to forty animals within a square kilometre. The highest densities have been in sitka spruce. More usually deer densities approximate to those on the open hill, ranging from five to twenty animals per square kilometre. Naturally these figures are approximate, and no accommodation has been made for the type of forestry, its age and growth, latitude, and the distribution of open glades and rides. The total number of reds in forestry is estimated to be between 30,000 and 50,000. Over and above which it must be pointed out that in a sense there is no such thing as a pure forestry population. Deer fences have been spectacularly overcome by red deer, and one stalker told me he had seen a red stag get his antlers twisted into the horizontal wires and uproot from the ground completely the deer posts on either side, proceeding afterwards to walk in leisurely vein through the gap. The fence was only just in place. I have seen this myself on an older fence. Alternatively deer walk over fence-lines after drifting snow has built a ramp. So. . . nothing is deer-proof, which has led some deer managers, so I am led to believe, to have resorted to woodland protection by spreading dung from carnivores round the perimeters. This says something surely, if it works, for the strength of ancestral memory. Forestry populations, therefore, have the ability to move to and fro, to some extent. On my own deer-fenced forestry the stags appear from tree-cover late in the rut. They walk the fence-line adjacent to the hill tracking out a muddy groove until the sounds of roaring rivals, and the wind-drifted musk of hinds in heat, can be tolerated no longer and they thrash their way out. Plantation owners have found that stags tend always to occupy higher up parts of the wood, and prefer the open glades. Deer numbers in trees shift with the age of the timber. Just after planting, forestry provides little cover and tree-planting operations have reduced the amount of feeding, but when trees are over three feet in height deer numbers increase until about thirty feet is attained. Forest canopy once established offers little opportunity for plant or grass growth and shrinks the useful habitat. When the trees are at 'pole' stage deer numbers usually decline. It is perhaps worth mentioning that although red deer damage trees they do not in any substantial way feed on trees or bark; when in forestry they rely for sustenance on ground vegetation. The densities of red deer related to populations in the same woodland of roe and sika are little-understood matters, and a fertile area for future study. My own impression, in a woodland containing roe and reds, is that instead of operating in segregated territories the two species partially overlap. It is possible the range of the roes has contracted as reds have become better established, but to separate out this factor from the shrinking of herbage would be a matter for scientific evaluation.

The high fecundity and low juvenile mortality of woodland-dwelling reds has already been mentioned. Birth dates and conception are thought to be the same inside the fence as outside. Where weights have been compared hinds have been about a third heavier and stags two-thirds heavier, but the comparison involved forestry red deer in England and kinder latitudes. It is true of all ungulates that males maximize body-weight advantage in better habitat more than females. Woodland deer in Sutherland consistently show heavier weights in cases I am familiar with, although I have noticed what is perhaps to be expected, that deer which have only recently come into the plantations experience a short-term falling-off in condition as they acclimatize. New woodland arrivals can be distinguished by the way branches brush loose hair from their coats.

Calves survive better in forestry, being beyond the reach of eagles and, mainly because shelter is superior. Radio-tracking has confirmed that woodland deer spend more of their time in the rides and clearings. Deer prefer browsing some tree species to others and the potential of Norway spruce to draw up a particular mineral from the ground makes it a pre-eminently popular target. The Forestry Commission use it as an attractor species, drawing attention away from other trees where forestry is unfenced. I have a small shelter-belt of Norways in the midst of a maze of deer-fences, but to my astonishment deer will leap cattle-grids and negotiate the hazards of walking the railway-line for considerable distances in order to thread their way to this little plot and thrash about the few trees with abandon. The absence of rowan, willow and aspen on open deer forest probably reflects deer's fondness for their flavours, although burning policies of the past, and the clearance of ground for sheep, will be factors too.

The deer in forestry equation affects open-hill deer management in a complex of ways. If deer colonize commercial woodlands and movements in and out of them fluctuate according to both population densities in the woods and the growth of the trees, then culling levels inside and outside the woods must somehow harmonize. This poses problems when the forestry owner is different to the deer forest owner. Channels of co-operation must be established. Assessments of the management needs will not be easy because under certain conditions the woods will act as a reservoir of deer for the open hill, and during hard weather deer will hide up in tree-shelter.

When deer are in the woods they are much harder to count; and pellets tell you a limited amount about the status of the animal that produced them. Overall, though, the findings of researchers about reds in forestry have told us useful things. The most important finding of all is the slowly-dawning realization that forestry blocks must be planned for deer, not against deer. Tree-growers must work with deer, not despite them. The presence of forestry means that in a worst-case scenario of winter deaths on the open hills there would still be a reservoir of original genetic stock from which emigration could occur. In today's climate of reaction against supernumerary deer it is hard to imagine the need arising for the repopulation of deer ranges. Biological history is too full of examples of population reversals, and evidence too strong of sharp short-term climatic changes, for us to be able to dismiss the possibility in some unpredictable future of needing to seek out native stocks of red deer to live again on the hills. Forestry-based reds will serve this function.

The taxonomy of red deer, however, has always been a vexed question. The species described as *Cervus elephus* has an enormous range extending from western Europe to central Asia, and is usually divided for convenience along the lines of geographical isolation. Twenty-five separate sub-species have been described, for instance in the red deer of Kashmir, Turkey, eastern Tibet and Corsica. The American elk, which correlates to the wapiti in Scandinavia, although capable of attaining weights four times that of the Scottish red deer, is regarded by many biologists as one of these sub-species. Red deer of British origin have been introduced into Argentina, New Zealand and Australia. The reason that the Scottish red is smaller than most of its cousins across the globe is habitat; the windswept, cold Highlands, with their covering of dwarf shrubs and rough grasses, stunt the development of Scottish deer, and with the climatic changes of the last few hundred years and colder climates prevailing, this has become more accentuated.

The lineage of man's utilization of deer is impressive. Neolithic man used deer antlers as digging picks and dressed himself in their skins. It is conjectured that pits were dug to trap deer and they were waylaid on forest trails. Successive human developments through the Bronze Age (which ended in Scotland around 250 BC) that drove deer from the woods in which they had grown to legendary size were: forest clearance for domestic stock and protection from wolves; the same effect was caused by shipbuilding from the thirteenth century on, and then in the seventeenth century tree-felling for smelting of iron. Other woodlands disappeared from natural causes, such as gales, sometimes followed by smothering from moss. The clachans, or pre-Clearance communities, used timbers as frameworks for the roofs of their black houses. Indigenous woodland now covers only one and a half per cent of Scotland.

All the while man has used the deer whose habitat he had progressively occupied. Early archaeological sites contain more remains of red deer than any other fauna. It has been reckoned that man's economic association with red deer goes back at least 15,000 years. It appears that larger animals were deliberately sought, and that deer fat was especially prized. Vegetation was burnt for deer, and it is thought possible ivy was cut for winter feeding. Antler velvet may have been used medicinally.

Moving to more recent time the earliest property rights in Scotland were hunting rights, established by the king for his own use. Red deer, as mentioned earlier, were the principal quarry. It is fascinating, in the light of the modern deer debate, to look back and study the rules applied to hunting and the deer. From the earliest records of King David's reign in the twelfth century, forest laws were devised to protect deer. Not only were the animals themselves sacrosanct, but so was their habitat. The ranging of goats, sheep and pigs was restricted, the toughest strictures being reserved for straying goats, in recognition of their potentially lethal effects on vegetation. The forest rangers were instructed to hang peripatetic goats by the horns in the trees, and if this failed their innards were to be displayed as a warning. A contemporary conservationist would have no quarrel with the principles established by this great Scottish king. For the forest laws were remarkable for their detail and scope, as well as the legendary severity of punishments for transgressors. Exact times when pasturers could be in the forests were laid down, both to protect pasture and to discourage any hanky-panky. Green timber was an inviolable commodity. Taking it unlawfully constituted one of the worst offences, punishable after 1424 by the forfeiture of eight cows. Taking protected wildflowers today is a prisonable offence, but no one can deny that compared to our forebears we are desultory conservationists. Mediaeval offenders could be maimed or financially ruined. The apparent readiness with which the hunting laws were accepted is not only owing to the treatments meted out to offenders. It is partly explained by the softening influence exerted from the old Gaelic culture, in which hunting was a well-understood and ubiquitous practice, on the newly-arrived Norman/ Flemish legislation-drafters. Scottish hunting laws were distinguished by more flexibility, less formalization, and more concessions to locals of lesser game, than corresponding regulations on the Continent and in England.

By 1474 it had become illegal to kill any deer under a year old, and a close season in winter had been set. Shortly after this the hunting tradition of the tinchel became established, in which glens and passes were cordoned off by armies of ghillies driving the deer on foot. This could take several days, at the climax of which the animals were channelled into corridors built of stone issuing into a high-walled enclosure. Here the Highlanders set about them with weapons varying from mighty axes to the dirks at their belts. Alternatively the deer were forced into narrow passes and then set upon with dogs. In a tinchel in Atholl attended by Queen Mary in 1563 it was recorded that 360 red deer were killed, in addition to two or three hapless Highlanders crushed as the frightened animals broke back. This cervine congregation took nearly two months to round up. Scenes such as these make the imagination boggle, but the physical backdrop to them in many places has hardly changed, and it is pondering this old history that can give such resonance to stalking days on the hills.

The next 200 years saw rapid changes in the Highlands, to which now all Scotland's deer had retreated. The old pre-Clearance system of land use, whilst appearing to observers to have been extremely primitive for the time, succeeded in making fertile some unpromisingly hostile hill-ground, and producing in its human community great fertility also. Even though the arable runrig agriculture covered only small areas of ground in the hills, the system was basically extensive. The small black cattle were moved up the hill and herded from shielings in the summer. Some of these shielings are still visible at around 3000 feet. The additional sheep and goats which completed the domestic stock in the clachan communities would have made use of a fair proportion of available range; few corners of the Highlands were not thus engaged to feed a human population that was growing steadily. Folk up the glens doubled in number in the fifty years up to 1880. Where then were the deer? Far back and far out seems to be the answer; guesswork suggests the bogs may have been the only ground they could call their own. By the 1780s the red deer population was at its lowest recorded ebb.

The era of the great sheep-walks occurred between 1780 and 1830, with the attendant Clearances and evictions carrying on sporadically after that. The deer perhaps fared better than the poor Highlanders; they were at least preserved in a few places specifically for hunting in what became known as deer forests. There were six left in 1811. In realms too desolate even for the desperate inhabitants of the early nineteenth century the deer may have eked out an existence also; parts of Sutherland still supported scanty numbers of them. The Cheviot and black-faced sheep were doughty foragers, and in the days of the flock-masters little grazing was left to deer.

The year 1833 was the year, according to the Earl of Malmesbury, that 'the Highlands became the rage'. The sport that brought it about was the modern equivalent of King David's pleasantest pastime, stalking deer, no longer on horseback but with a rifle. By 1842 there were forty forests set aside for deer; by the turn of the century most of the Highlands was so utilized. Much has been made in recent time of the smaller stature of red deer today and of those that the Victorians hunted. But when it is considered that the deer range expanded onto a landscape that only forty years earlier had been blessed by the careful, laborious, long-term enrichment of the earth by generations of toiling Highlanders, it is perhaps not surprising that, with few competitors for food, some of the deer got themselves into impressive shape.

The history of Victorian and Edwardian sport is another story. A little-mentioned aspect is that the image of the red stag gained in substance. Once more, with Sir Edwin Landseer's painting 'The Monarch of the Glen', the stag took on some of the mystique, the essence of sentient wildness in a fellow mammal, which lurked in our ancestral memory since the time that early man had relied on this animal more than any other. Turn of the century stalking became a celebration of the stag and inspired much that is still obstinately buried in our Scottish culture. By 1912 around 3,600,000 acres of Scotland was established as deer forest, constituting a monoculture which had attracted political criticism. It is thought around 9000 stags and hinds were shot annually in the 1890s; before the Second World War this figure was 18,000, with approximately even numbers of both sexes. This rough statistical outline can be completed with figures from the Agricultural Statistics (1957) Scotland which recognized a total of 183 deer forests, covering some 2,800,000 acres. The two counties with most forests were Inverness with fifty-two and also the largest area under deer forest, followed by Ross and Cromarty with fifty. Sutherland was the county with the next largest concentration of deer forest, followed by Argyll then Perthshire. In the present time definitions have been somewhat blurred, partly by over-enthusiastic property-selling agents describing anything onto which red deer have wandered as a deer forest, also because large forests have been split up. Those with the best idea of what constitutes a deer forest today are the stalking tenants, who put their hand in their pocket to back their assessments.

What is meant by a deer forest? It derives from the medieval term 'afforestation' which meant setting aside an area for hunting. The process of afforestation involved clearing the ground of stock, which after the Clearances were represented by sheep and cattle. In today's terms most deer forests are partly or entirely used by sheep as well as deer, and the term forest has gradually changed to embrace this. As deer are presently moving more and more onto grouse-moors, and filling in as Highland sheep hirsels are closed, the term has come to have an elastic meaning. An early afforested area might or might not have had trees on it. The fact that today deer forests, by and large, are windswept unsheltered treeless expanses is made more poignant by the debate that rages about them concerning exactly that: should there be trees in the forest?

My knowledge of how deer forests were delineated derives from having been stalking on a few, and impressions gained about the boundaries or 'marches' as they are termed. On many deer forests the marches remain unchanged since they were first drawn. It is noticeable that descriptions in legal documents of marches often vary in small ways from estate maps which were drawn up simultaneously, but perhaps without the benefit of practical knowledge of the ground. Deer forests need to be big. There is no rule-of-thumb size because ground differs from place to place; clearly the stony summits of hills can seldom be of use to deer; nor can lochs. What determines the ground's usefulness for deer is the mosaic of herbage and the availability of shelter. A deer forest must be large enough to support resident populations of both stags and hinds. It is no accident that the largest forests are run most professionally and commercially. The deer are available for sporting uses for a longer time. The stag shooting season starts on 1 July and the hind season, coinciding with the culmination of the stags on 20 October, ends on 15 February. Although in practice not all of this time is utilized, deer managers on large deer forests have wider parameters within which to work. The smaller forests will not reliably have deer on the ground at all times, or they will be of the wrong sex at the wrong time. So, the deer forest area is generally large. The forests in east and central Sutherland with which I am familiar are at least 20,000 acres, which proves to be a sufficient area for practical management, and also large enough to allow a stalking party on the ground wherever the wind hails from. Smaller patches would restrict stalking flexibility, and there would be a tendency for the deer to be on the ground only periodically. Waylaying deer in narrow corridors constrained by unhelpful marches is no way to stalk. The experience demands that the theatre of action is big enough for a proper day on the hill. Further south in the Highlands, with mineral-rich terrain, deeper glens and better shelter, the deer would not need to travel so much, and smaller areas would suffice. Generally speaking the agents, or factors, who subdivided the enormous landholdings of the old Highland chiefs into deer forests knew what they were about. The forests were large enough for sporting purposes. The problems of distance, which our all-terrain vehicles minimize today, were dealt with then by the erection of stalking lodges situated on the edge of the forest area. Deer stalking parties might repair there for a few days at a time. The one at Borrobol was five miles from the lodge, and travel to it was by pony and trap. From it, at a distance of three miles, a flag-pole could be detected with a telescope, and when the ghillie whose office it was to scan the outer ground for deer raised the flag, the sporting party quaffed the last of their liquor, snatched their rifles, and sallied forth. I digress. A deer forest of character wants not for space.

The marches were a combination of hill-tops, rivers and watersheds. In Sutherland where there is so much undulating and amorphous-looking moorland, where the peat-lands appear to roll with a repetitive swell for miles without impediment, some of the marches are hard to precisely define until you are standing on the line of them, and can see which way the water is draining. More rugged country was easier to divide up, although sometimes, to the annoyance of stalkers since, the march has been drawn up the middle of a steep corrie, and is therefore frequently of little use to either side – unless they approach from their neighbour's territory. In open country the delineation of marches can seem itself an absurdity, and I have been to few forests where in one corner or another a march is not in dispute. But usually the disputes have rumbled on harmlessly for generations of stalkers, where failure to take up the time-honoured cudgels might be viewed by the keepering fraternity as 'losing ground'. Ground, to put it mildly, has always stirred high emotions in the Highlands, and it is a matter of curiosity that the famous quarrels of crofters over inch by inch definition of the boundary-fence are repeated just as fiercely when the subject is a featureless tract of open hill. One of the more pointless human vanities, happily rare, has been the fencing-in of deer forests on a large scale, taking away from the enclosed area the signal charm of the Highland land-mass, that its wild beauty stretches uninterrupted from coast to coast, and taking from the deer their status as free agents.

The question of fencing introduces that part of the red deer's role which is neither biological study nor sporting. This is deer's relations with man outside the deer forest, mostly reflected in deer legislation referring to impacts on agriculture. Wandering deer, almost exclusively stags searching for food and shelter in winter, have been a problem for neighbours of deer forests from the beginning. Even in mediaeval times the monarch some-times compensated smallholders for agricultural damage. Between 1872 and 1919 there were five government enquiries which referred to deer, some concerned with compensation for those suffering deer damage, some with the extension of agricultural production onto deer forests. The latter concluded by-and-large that such efforts would be fruitless. In 1959 an act of Parliament was passed creating the Red Deer Commission, the basic remit of which was to act as the government's reporter and regulator on deer matters in Scotland. Close seasons for red deer were introduced, and powers to protect agri-culture and forestry were increased. The right of agricul-tural occupiers to shoot trespassing deer on enclosed land had already been established in the Agriculture

(Scotland) Act of 1948. The Red Deer Commission (RDC) itself was empowered to kill deer, and to authorize others to shoot deer at night if special situations demanded it. The RDC counts deer numbers and has done since its inception. Between 1961 and 1970, 80 per cent of deer range in the Highlands was counted, providing the first proper estimates of the population. Counting techniques were at first disputed by stalkers, and have been made less fallible since. Red deer range is now divided for counting into some fifty different blocks. The RDC monitors the culls and has statutory access to game-dealers' records. For the first time in the winter of 1992–3 the commission's stalkers participated in culling on estates, spending four weeks in the heavily-overstocked glens of east Angus. There are twelve commissioners from a variety of organizations including landowners and conservationists, and a chairman who serves for three years; all are appointed by the Secretary of State for Scotland.

The most ticklish matter has been the shooting of deer on enclosed ground, a concession to farmers and crofters suffering from marauders. The weak definition of what constituted enclosed ground has led to abuses which have often benefited local communities, and have certainly provided many Highland hotels and restaurants with meat delivered to the back door, often fresh to the point of being still warm, and tradeable for a few pounds or pints. It would be interesting to know how many smallholders living near deer ranges would, in a blind tasting, be unable to identify the taste of venison. Most could not have bought it over the counter as the Highland butcher is famously averse to presenting venison, either because it detracts attention from his mainstream beef range, or because the meat is sufficiently in circulation anyway. Some croft-holdings, neglecting to mend the fence whilst industriously growing turnips as winter approaches, have graduated to actually describing themselves as estates. Perhaps in terms of venison volumes they are.

The poaching of deer is not seen in Highland communities as a particularly heinous crime, and is frequently tacitly condoned. Where there is more heightened feeling is at the commercial end of deer poaching, involving highly-armed gangs travelling in a cavalcade. Their antics are a demonstration, if it is needed, that night-shooting of deer is rightly a very sensitive subject. Wounded animals cannot be followed up and are discovered, as daylight breaks, expiring in agonies or limping about the landscape. Both the police and the courts, particularly in recent years, have in some areas taken a tougher stand against commercial-scale poaching; but the indicator which determines poaching levels is always principally the price of venison. Thus it is, as venison prices have languished, that some traditionally hyper-active poaching grounds have actually quietened down. Firearms legislation may have helped this process along. Nonetheless deer poaching is an endemic and eternal Highland activity, as all insiders know. It was a west-coaster who, on being apprehended nocturnally dragging a deer out of the heather with its feet draped over his shoulders, began pretending to fight it off, shouting, 'Off me! Get away from me!' as if the cadaver was an over-affectionate assailant. Poaching has little relevance for deer populations, unless carried out on a massive scale, because it takes stags rather than the population-determinant hinds. The scale of deer poaching is consistently underestimated by outsiders who pore over theoretical statistics, with one possible exception – the officers of the Inland Revenue. Having suddenly discovered a new source of funds the Revenue's men have been studying more closely the accounts of game-dealers. This led to a recent case in which, despite the necessary haziness of the exact details, the bruited-about figures gave cause for contemplation. Four highly-motivated farmers in a certain area were presented out-of-the-blue with tax demands on the basis of having marketed some 2000 deer carcasses. Whether or not these deer actually moved, in antedeluvian numbers, onto the farms in question and were shot legally as marauders, became academic. The point was the Revenue could prove money had been received for them. Heavy selling of farm-stock ensued to pay the tax demands.

The principal reason poaching figures have never been realistically assessed is that it is in no one's interests to do it. The RDC calculates a figure for poached venison, but has no way of knowing the full story. What adorns citizen's dinner-plates each evening is not yet a concern of the state. Not every game-dealer's books are exactly biblical either. A fish farmer of my acquaintance visited a Highland game-dealer to offer fishy products. As they drove in the morning through empty moorland the game-dealer slammed on the brakes, drew up a rifle which had been lying on the floor at the back of the car and knocked down a deer grazing close by. He threw it in the boot and calmy proceeded, watchful for more opportunities. The world is not short of poachers who have become affluent after years of night-shifts; some bought deer ground themselves and then protected it with exemplary diligence. A rogue sheriff recently muddied the waters further by declaring that all ground could be regarded as enclosed, effectively pronouncing that every man-jack and his maid could come and dispose of the marauders. The Highlands has always had its share of mavericks. This is the background to the debate on deer, and I describe it because to ignore the location in which new manoeuvres are proposed is to drift into the abstract. Also it is a fact that what happens to Scotland's red deer concerns not only forestry managers, farmers and deer forest owners, stalkers and sportsmen, but the community at large as well. More people have a vested interest in the deer than is officially the case.

So stands the red deer today, fondly regarded by those who get dividends from it, prized and protected by the sportsmen, the most deeply-studied and analysed British mammal, and one which is used by as many modern logo-creators as it once was by family genealogists looking for heraldic emblems. It has become too numerous in some places, a matter which is being presently addressed, but also a matter which has given rise to a call for reconsideration of its role, possibly to limit its range and reduce its profile. The first area to look at is the red deer on the deer forest, where its management has implications for jobs, local economies and ecologies, and land use in the widest sense. For, to a degree, knowing what the deer are for and how we should interact with them, is a test of our wider relationship with nature. The answer to the deer debate is one we get wrong at our peril.

# Chapter 3

The case for deer forests will never be won on direct employment figures. However, employment in stalking is perhaps a model example of why bald figures conceal more than they convey. The bald figure is that there are around 320 professional stalkers in Scotland. These are the men, and currently one woman, who know what a deer is thinking of doing when the thought is a mere shadow. But self-evidently 320 stalkers did not bring home all 60,000 red deer carcasses that were shot in the 1992–3 season. The fact is that engaged in stalking over the course of the season are a multitude of assistants, part-timers, trainees, students, shepherds and so on. They act as ghillies, pony-boys, or stalkers themselves. The official figure is for about 516 'full-time job equivalents', as employment statisticians are prone to call them. But this is still insufficient. On most deer forests there are people periodically out stalking who appear in no statistics.

My own case is a typical one. I stalk one half of the forest during the hind-shooting season, another stalker the other half. Each of us has a vehicle driver, one of whom is an underkeeper, the other of whom is a shepherd helping out. When the stalker is not using the underkeeper he is assisted by the farm manager. Of these five people only two appear in the lists of keepering job-holders. Other forests have similar arrangements. Another estate I know of has a stalking team comprising the owner husband and wife, and daughter. Yet they will not describe themselves as gamekeepers. Further to this is the contentious matter of tenants being asked as a duty of the tenancy to take culls of females. This is a highly unsatisfactory short-cut opted for by landowners who are unable to afford a stalker and wish, nonetheless, to achieve their full cull. In practice the females are not shot, stalking tenants being more interested in the male of the species, but disinclined to forgo the freedom of an open-ended sort of sporting lease. The shortcomings of this are another question: the point is that tenants on stalking grounds are doing the job of stalkers and replacing them. Last are the contract stalkers who appear seasonally on deer forests either to conduct culls or to assist them. These components of the active stalking community generally have main jobs in other spheres.

There is a more important aspect of stalker employment. Rather than enumerating the jobs to reach useful conclusions, consider what jobs they are. They are professional wildlife managers in the remotest, most exposed parts of the British Isles. In that they perform a culling and conservation job, which is ultimately under statutory control (through the RDC's power of enforcing a cull), they are servants of the state as well as the boss. Consider too the burdens placed upon them by the terms of the 1981 Countryside and Wildlife Act. One of these makes it an offence to damage freshwater mussels. It is an offence to rob eagle's nests, steal rare protected wildflowers, kill wildcats, disturb badgers at their setts, and a host of things. The stalker is the only person on the ground in a position to notice transgressions against this important act in many situations. Who else is likely to pose a threat to egg-thieves in targeting the nests of Schedule I rare breeding birds such as black-throated divers, or scoters, on the dubh lochs of the northern Highlands? Above all, without the stalker who would care for the deer? It is not how many stalkers are there that matters, but where are they working, and do their duties overlap with anyone else's? The answer is that stalkers are some of the only people living where they do. They occupy the highest-altitude houses in Scotland, a fact often noted with extreme relief by disoriented mountaineers. Without them the apparent emptiness would be emptier.

I mentioned the figure of 60,000 red deer carcasses for the winter of 1992–3. It is a huge figure, the highest ever recorded for the Scottish red deer cull. The revenue earned by all this venison is the prime income-source for deer forests, sometimes equalled but rarely exceeded by the value of sporting rents. Aside from what is sold, good natural protein is provided for a wide range of people. It is reckoned that eight per cent of the annual venison crop is eaten, as it were, 'in-house'.

The venison trade recently fell into such disrepair that it threatened seriously to undermine the whole economy of deer forests. The price quoted as the venison price is what game-dealers will pay to pick carcasses up, usually still in their skins, from the deer-larder door. In 1989 this dropped to 35 pence a pound, approximately the same in pence as it fetched twenty years previously, or a drop in value of several hundred per cent. In the early 1970s the venison price was £1 per pound, a plateau it has never since reached. Selling venison for sub-offal prices swept away the motives for deer forest owners to cull hinds hard (a minority culled harder to make up for low prices by higher numbers). Traditionally the hind venison cheque had paid the stalker's wages over winter. Hind-culling in the late 1980s became an onerous and expensive activity. More stalkers were laid off and deer forest owners got wound into a cycle of slack manage-ment; the wheel turned full-circle when it became apparent that hind numbers had rocketed up, a trend perceived by the RDC some years earlier. The persistently abject venison price was the underlying factor which set in motion the fashion for questioning the role of deer forests, and started what was to be termed the red deer crisis.

The year 1993 is a crossroads in red deer management in a number of ways and one of them is a change in the value of venison, or to be more accurate a change in the image of venison which may improve the long-term value. First it is necessary to understand the venison market in which estates operate. There are three major dealers, a diversity which several years ago looked like disappearing. A group of far-sighted landowners, afraid of venison falling into the maw of a monopolistic dealership, formed their own co-operative. Other traditional dealers were scornful. The meat trade is a notoriously rough environment and the men in tweed suits 'would be minced up' was the common prediction. It did not turn out that way. Highland Venison entered the market-place, attempted to arrange guaranteed orders from its constituent members, and gradually established itself. The difficulties of dealing in venison are to do with the curious structure of the trade. To secure the fidelity of suppliers the dealers have to name their price at the start of the season, and hold it. Because of the topsy-turvy nature of the business, the volume importance of the export market (traditionally to Germany), and fluctuating exchange rates, it was hard for dealers to do this. If they allowed too much room for profit, someone would come along in the middle of the season, and offer their clients more. Inducements to stalkers, expected to bend the ear of their employers, were used quite openly by rival dealers to secure supplies. Highland Venison's advantage was that the suppliers owned the business. Walking the knife-edge of tough competition, exacerbated by the opening-up of eastern Europe and their huge venison resource, Highland Venison survived the critical days of judgement when venison prices lapsed ignominiously, and came of age in January 1993 when it entered an agreement with the supermarket chain Safeways to supply wild game in a promotion to sell the most natural British meat, low in calories and cholesterol, and strong on flavour.

Safeways took a punt on venison and, in the first year of trading, is winning it. Its popularity has exceeded expectations, and their fresh venison is retailing at the time of writing at a level of £30,000 worth per week. The product was scrutinized by Safeways health and hygiene inspectors, open-hill stalking methods were examined (the chairman went stalking on a deer forest), and great thought was put into the launch. Venison appeared on Safeways shelves in eleven different forms, from steaks to sausages. For the deer forest owners the supermarket launch has underpinned prices, which have inched back from the brink to 60p to 75p a pound. Of the three main dealers Highland has about a third of the whole wild venison market and the others make up to 75 per cent of the total. Around a dozen other small dealers dodge and shift between the big three, making pickings where they can with lower overheads. The factor which enables small dealerships to survive, even thrive, is the grey area of poached supplies. Typically these are bought by dealers for as little as half the going open-market rate, giving them room for attractive margins.

The large number of deer shot over winter in 1992–3, added to a small lift in the venison price, meant that the money paid to producers amounted to around £3.5 million. This is the equivalent, approximately, at wholesale prices of £7 million, a sum, in the cash-deficient Highland economy, not to be sniffed at. Furthermore it is a sum unsupported by any government subsidy (although state funds have helped dealerships meet modern hygiene regulations). The by-products of these deer carcasses – pizzles (stags only), hooves, tails etc. – are worth a further quarter of a million pounds. The antlers, retained by the stalkers as a perk when the shooters do not want them, the tusks (upper molars), and sinews, are sold by stalkers at season's end, or hoarded for retirement or a rainy day. The teeth of deer must be one of the most esoteric futures markets in the world. These accessories, when not used by craft shops, are exported to the Orient, a matter regarded too often as risible for its association with aphrodisiacs. In the Far East parts of deer have been used medicinally for thousands of years, and modern medical science is now finding the practices have been far from unselective. Skins are sold separately too, although as the hind season wears on they become spoiled from warble flies.

The marketing of Scottish venison by Safeways marks a new departure in the Highlands. It is a short time ago that Scottish venison exported to Germany simply piled up in huge mountains of anonymous deer-meat, mixed with venison from Poland, east Germany or wherever, undifferentiated in age, sex or species. Red deer calves, about the size of a roe deer, are sold as such still, eluding the trade descriptions acts. Forestry deer, which are not heather-fed, are still sold along with hill deer, for there are limits to the discrimination of the contemporary palate. More seriously, New Zealand farmed venison is sold through British multiples under the name of the English processing company, parading as home-grown. For there is a premium for the home-grown, wild product, where distinctions are drawn, and confusing the two is profitable. But this is a deceit the like of which is almost ubiquitous in meat distribution in Britain. New Zealand, with its farmed output of 12,000 tonnes compares powerfully with Scotland's modest, and unenlargeable, 1600 tonnes of wild meat. But dealers reckon the New Zealand product has helped stabilize prices, and created the possibility, at best, of a two-tier commodity.

Not only the marketing of venison has been brought up-to-date. Culling practices and the larder-work performed by stalkers have improved immeasurably. In days gone by deer culled on the high tops were from time-to-time got to lower elevations by the simple expedient of rolling them down cliff-faces. In-skin mince lay crumpled at the bottom and was hauled home. No longer. Carcass presentation standards are now unrecognizably higher, an achievement connected to the introduction by Highland Venison of grading. Badly-shot or badly-handled carcasses are downgraded, and the payment rates slide away uncomfortably. Kerry Keysell, managing director of Highland, said that when he and an old professional vet were grading carcasses in February 1993 they were condemning as unfit for human consumption some carcasses that eight years ago would have been of average quality. The better quality meat allows the processors to do more with it, extracting fancy cuts, and generally maximizing its potential more effectively. Furthermore it widens the gap with New Zealand venison, which is farmed and therefore frozen, and has travelled round the world to arrive on the British plate. The availability of better-quality wild venison has swelled the numbers of those engaged in the Highlands in venison processing, now thought to be over 100.

The key factor in deer forests' economics is, in my view, the price of venison. If this had fallen any lower than the depths plumbed in 1989 it would have become uneconomic for some remote forests to bring the meat home. Leaving them lying on the hill would have been a welcome innovation for eagles, foxes and crows; for landowners it would have been a public relations disaster. EC regulations have already outlawed sheep and cattle carcasses left lying out; they would have moved swiftly onto deer. If, perchance, venison values were to rise again there would be two contradictory impacts. Poaching would rapidly increase, and deer forest owners would be able to take on more stalkers. One way or another it would substantially alter the financial equations. At present the only benefits being gained from the low price, the supermarket launch aside, are for local communities served through the nearest estate deer-larder with fresh venison. But EC regulations on larder hygiene standards, typically wallowing in overkill, threaten to knock this out by forcing back-door sales to close down – or go underground. Already EC laws are hastening the next stage in streamlining wild venison production by introducing carcass-chilling standards and outlawing the traditional practices of hanging meat to tenderize it. In future it seems probable that collection centres with chilling facilities will replace the visiting game-van, sooner for remote forests. This will pose problems for stalkers, required to drive meat out at the end of a tiring day which probably reached the deer-larder only after dark. Co-operation between estates, never a famously easy thing, could come part of the way to a rescue.

The sale of venison is only one of two big sources of income for deer forests. The second is sporting revenue from rented stalking. Attempts to estimate the value of this have usually understated it, often getting lost in reckonings of how many stalking days are actually let. A better way of looking at it is to estimate the number of potentially marketable stags. For if the deer forest owner and his family elect to do the stalking, or some of it, it is a reasonable assumption that, without it, they would do their stalking elsewhere. Whoever does the stalking does not affect the potential value. The overworked RDC has, at time of writing, not calculated precise stag culls for the 1992 season. But in 1991, 15,550 stags were shot in Scotland during the stalking season; a further 1911 were reported shot outside it. The 15,550 figure theoretically represents all those stags that could be let. This includes the forestry cull, much of which will in practice not be let, and low-value sporting stags such as early-season ones still in velvet. Sporting rents for 1992–3 are pitched between £220 and £250 per stag, with considerably higher rates being paid in special situations and on major deer forests. Taking a mean average of £235 per stag, Scottish stag stalking is worth around £3.7 million annually. The proportion of stag stalking let for sport is sharply increasing.

What is the state of the stalking market in 1993? Despite the enthusiasm for stalking in general the market for open-hill deer stalking is 'dodgy' in the phrase of one leading agent. Most newcomers cut their teeth on roe deer, by far Britain's most numerous species. Possibly the sheer physical discomforts of open-hill stalking have limited appeal. The packaging of high-seat stalking, with a flask of sloe-gin in one hand, binoculars in the other, a surgically-precise shot from a fixed position, is a preferable marketing challenge to that of a soaked, chilled, prostrate body snaking painfully through disagreeably rough country, rain beating on his person, pinned down all the while by a staring stag. The market in Scottish red deer stalking got overturned by the break-up of eastern Europe in 1989. Stags were available there for sweetie-money. Shot from horse-drawn carts, or even from sputtering automobiles, they nonetheless had large enough heads to look respectable on the wall of the average hunting cabin. In 1993 you can go there and shoot five or six of these for £500, accommodation inclusive. Furthermore you are doing your bit for the resurrection of 'old' Europe – many of them are marauding on agricultural ground. It is hard for Scotland to contend. On the other hand the east European stalking may not endure so cheaply for long; the main areas are in danger of shooting themselves out. In time the desperation for western currency will abate.

Times were when the Highland tradition was a big positive plus factor. The experienced sport letting agent

Neil Ramsay surprised me by saying this did not count at all any longer. He believes there is a weariness with tartanry, a fact uncomfortably dawning on tourist boards in Scotland as well. The American market is possibly the only exception to this. The Americans tend to want one big stag, which is difficult for Scottish forests to provide. On the other hand some other Americans, brought up in the tradition of one stag each, maybe for a whole year, relish the chance of getting out every day for a week, and facing afresh the problems of how to get close enough for the shot. One of the constraints on Scottish stalking is the small number of nationalities which constitutes the market, and within those countries the small number of 'hunters' able and willing to travel to reach stalking. To the European hunters, mostly Germans, Swiss and Belgians, can be added Americans, Australians, Norwegians, Canadians, New Zealanders and Swedes. The main market for stalking tenants remains the British them-selves, although there is a shortage of young people coming into the sport. The shrinking units of the British army were once the recruiting grounds for keen young stalkers. One of the problems is that stalking is a less high-value rental proposition for sporting agents than either salmon fishing or grouse shooting. Fifteen per cent of the value of a stag let for £250 is not a king's ransom. A week's driven grouse shooting is serious pickings in comparison. This has militated against stalking being actively promoted by Scottish agents; it tends to tag in behind the higher-profile alternatives.

Hind-stalking is increasingly popular, especially in the home market, but there are constraints to its operation. The first is practical. With the larger hind culls of the last two or three years, stalkers trying to get the job done effi-ciently and within the seasonal time-frame do not relish having a hind-shooting tenant hanging round their necks. It takes longer to stalk in to hinds with a paying client, there are a higher proportion of aborted stalks, the amateur rifleman is unable to select hinds as fast as professionals, and his shooting is inferior. Where a professional stalker might, on occasion, manage to take six selected hinds from a group the visiting outsider might only manage three, or none. In general terms the weather is inclement and unpredictable, fog or snow can wipe days out, travel to and from the forest is dodgy, and stalkers find it difficult to provide a similar sporting service to the customary one in the stag season. The hind-shooting is primarily a cull, and some stalkers are sensitive to visitors helping with their work, and forking out to do so. On the other hand there is much to be said for hind-shooting for visiting rifles.

There is growing demand for stalking. Its popularity has trebled in eight years. Although hind-shooting is going in at the deep end, the skills that are required in identifying age classes, condition, and general health are solid gains. It is going about stalking, as it were, from the stalkers end. If it is sometimes uncomfortable, chillingly wintry and emotionally draining to shoot animals in large numbers, so be it. It is also rewarding. If placing the shot, having dropped the two cull hinds which had stood broadside, and waiting for the rest of the group to stop milling around, when finally the target animal is diagonally on, is tough on the nerves, then at least the rifleman finds out what shooting deer under pressure is all about. If he shoots an animal cleanly through the chest, when it is front on, looking slightly downhill, and evidently a ragged-looking hind which needs removing, only to find when he arrives to gralloch it that two stumps protrude between the ears, then he learns that sensation familiar to all hind shooters, when a hind at 150 yards turns out to be a knobber (young stag) at ten. In this day and age sportsmen are encouraged to know their quarry; no one will ever get to know deer by shooting only the males. In the meantime, let hind-shooting is good for estate finances. The figure is rising every year but when reviewed in 1989 it was found that 16 per cent of the hind cull was let to tenants. Rents in 1993 are typically about £60 a day, with an extra £20 for each animal shot.

Apart from stalkers' inconvenience there are structural reasons not to let hind-shooting. The principal one is that once income is being taken for hind-shooting the rating assessor pricks up his ears, calculates the potential letting value of the hind cull, puts the figures into his black box, which spits out a rating assessment. The possibility of higher rates puts people off letting hind-stalking. Already rates are levied by local authorities at punishing levels, indirectly curbing deer forests' efficiency at conducting culls, and acting as a brake on employment. Present rateable values are £100 for each stag shot for sport, on which sum so many pennies of poundage are charged, typically around 47 pence in the pound. Therefore a deer forest shooting 100 stags for sports would pay £4700 as an annual contribution to local public finances; return services specifically for deer forests do not exist.

An enterprising estate owner situated on the starkly remote peninsula of Knoydart recently braved the ratings courts by appealing against rates applied to deer forests *per se*. His argument was that the basis of sporting rents on Highland deer forests was out of date. The basis of the assessor's figures is the putative rental value of the stag stalking season. However the Valuation and Rating Act (Scotland) 1956 states that such a lease should include an obligation by the tenant to pay all expenses – insurance, repairs, rates themselves – sufficient to maintain the land in a state to command such a rent. The landowner then advertised his property, having computed what these costs would be, and, not surprisingly, found that there were no takers. For having money to blow as a deer forest owner is a different thing from blowing it without the satisfaction of ownership and management. No deer forests are let annually any longer – one of the anachronisms the landowner objected to. As the appeal was being mounted by one individual, and the Inland Revenue starred a Queen's Counsel in their defence, the result was unfavourable to the landowner. The point, nonetheless is clear. Rates are flogging a horse which is near death. Another point is that local authorities will fight hard not to lose this trouble-free source of revenue.

The costs of owning deer forests at prevailing venison and stalking values are prodigious. Naturally owners are not rushing forward to announce the scale to which they subsidize their sporting assets, but it is thought there are no pure deer forest properties which turn in a regular annual profit, even ones operating as commercially as possible. Hugh Rose, secretary of the British Deer Society in Scotland, a contract stalker himself, and thoroughly conversant with the scene, has a rule-of-thumb measurement of costs. Disadvantaged west coast forests, possibly dependent on access by boat, or at the end of long tracks, could cost up to £4 an acre a year; mainstream west coast forests £3 an acre, and in the eastern and central Highlands, with the support of revenue from grouse-moors, the figure might be £2. The truth of this comparison is best verified by looking at land-ownership patterns; in the western Highlands the big forests are mostly owned by individuals or families renowned for their depth of pocket. Of course deer forests would never change hands if owning them was inevitably as punitive as Hugh Rose's figures suggest; but in many unfortunate cases the financial realities of ownership are learnt the hard way. Others diversify, often ingeniously, to lessen the impact of deer losses. Some estates make money. There are huge disparities, in keeping with a various land. Nonetheless the figures present a stark picture, possibly an unsustainable one.

So what do you have? An asset which routinely loses money, which is unsubsidized, which is selectively penalized by fiscal ravages levied in the absence of alternative sources of public sector funding, which employs people in remote locations where there is no other employment, producing a resource which is chronically undervalued. It is worth looking at the surrounding ambience, other land-uses, and other people. Deer forests and sheep herdings have been intertwined in their histories since the Clearances. When deer forests were cleared of sheep the clearance was only partial in many places; most ground which could support a sheep hirsel kept one. Most forests had an inner ground grazed by sheep, and in summer the sheep ranged out, picking their way on long summer afternoons from herb to herb right out onto the deer ground. Depending on the way they were herded, the activeness with which the sheep were moved onto higher ground in summer evenings, and their general deployment by shepherds to keep ground fresh, or indeed from reversion to lower-variety swards, this worked well. The deer and the sheep are complementary grazers in many respects, the sheep nipping down neater than the deer, and the deer keeping cropped the heather that would otherwise grow ragged and leggy and beyond sheep's reach. This equation, made complete by the presence of cattle that graze off the rougher grass-clumps which sheep and deer leave behind, enriches pasture and promotes plant diversity, and is now seriously threatened.

The reason is the European Community's Common Agricultural Policy, or CAP. A reform package has been agreed and put in place. The formula for hill sheep is a short-term increase in subsidies peaking in 1993, followed by a steady phasing out of support. There is no provision for subsidy protection after 1996. As things stand this will simply result in the close-down of hill farming in Scotland, not a political objective anyone has been straining to articulate. Subsidy for the most disadvantages areas, regarded as a form of social payment, amounts to two-thirds of income. Hill farmers are already at the end of the rope. Lamb prices were as high in 1980 as in 1992, whilst all costs have risen. Wool is almost valueless, hardly worth clipping off sheep's backs. It once constituted a third of farm income for Highland flock-masters. Furthermore the policy agreed in Brussels seems designed to target the only Scottish sheep farmers capable of competing after 1996; those with over 1000 ewes are deprived of full subsidy in the run-up period during which producers are supposed to be bracing themselves for the brave new world. So, in theory, the Scottish sheep farmer will compete after 1996 with the New Zealand sheep rancher, running 1000 ewes to the New Zealanders' 10,000, his beasts picking out a hard living from the rough, mineral-deficient northern hemisphere moorland, instead of mowing contentedly over the finest grazing sward in the world. A similar picture of inequity applies to the economics of hill cattle.

Of course it is all unthinkable, possibly because it is unthought about. It would require a politician with a neck of brass, and a misconception of the extent to which the hills are valued by society at large, to allow the hill sheep sector to fold up entirely. Upland dereliction from Cornwall to Caithness is not the sort of platform any political canvasser wants in the backdrop. Furthermore there is no evidence the public wants to strip out hill farmers' supports, for the meagre amount they cost the state exchequer. After 1996 national governments will come up with some system of their own for keeping the hill-dwellers *in situ*, and whether it is called an environment payment or a sheep subsidy is unimportant. The point to all this, however, is how it affects red deer. Certainly as the transitions occur deer will spot the gaps,

and occupy sheep ground when time has let fresh grasses
through. Already many deer forests have swollen at the
edges as sheep flocks have marched to market and away.
There was a cycle of sheep numbers falling in the late
1960s and mid-70s and the second cycle is now under
way. The critical deer over-population areas in the early
1990s were frequently places where sheep and cattle had
been cleared. Nature, as always, hates a vacuum. And
deer are fast colonists. For the future, the sheep population will affect the equation for deer directly. It is pur-
poseless to look at herbage management on the hill in
terms of one species only. Meaningful assessments are of
total grazing pressures, married to calculations about the
direction of vegetation changes because of climate.
Climate also affects the densities and varieties of insects
which live in heather and eat it. Sheep and deer are
merely the most conspicuous factors in a complex environmental cocktail. At present it looks as if sheep's
share of the moorland habitat is being reduced. Attitudes
to deer must take this factor into account.

Another subsidy-dependent land-use affecting red deer
is forestry. We have seen in a few years one of the
sharpest about-turns in a state planning policy ever to
have tested the trackers of fashion. I remember ten years
ago talking about amenity tree species as they were then
known, open glades in commercial plantations,
hardwoods, and other monstrosities which were seen by
commercial timber men as wasting useful productive
ground, and being met with a wall of silence by civil
servants who had been disciplined to think in monocultures. Deer were to be killed out not planned in. Killed
out, moreover, without the space to see them. In 1993
commercial timber production, previously the illustrious
sole objective, is down at the bottom of the list of objectives. A state forester looking over a Woodland Grant
Scheme (the bread-and-butter small plantation scheme) is

apt to advise an expansion of the area left unplanted,
boosting the 'open ground' proportion of the block. The
block is itself a hangover word from the bad old days.
Trees can no longer be planted in blocks. Forest edges
must be feathered, made to look naturalistic. Woodland
Grant schemes must blend with adjacent land uses, even
land features far off. As for monocultures of spruce or
lodgepole pine, forget it. Big blocks of a thousand acres,
plonked onto open landscape, will either be torn apart
by the various consultative bodies, or dismantled in
advance by the Forestry Authority. Native species are all
the rage. Speak birch, oak, alder, willow, rowan, Scots
pine, hazel, and you are on track. 'Exotics', meaning
imported species like spruce, are to be employed only if
their impact can be softened with environmentally-
friendly 'natives'. Some of the distinctions are close to
being precious: surely beech, guilty of arriving in Britain
as recently as a thousand years ago, has by now become
naturalized? Old-timers in the forest service have been re-
programmed. They emerge from new training courses
with not only new perspectives, but a new language to
express them in.

The volte-face is right and long overdue. We are indeed
a nation in its infancy when it comes to growing mass
softwoods for pulping. Had we looked at the European
models, countries with far more forest cover, with longer
experience of tree-growing, with an embedded, hard-won
knowledge of woodland ecology starting with deer, we
could have avoided naive mistakes. The north Highlands,
for example, might not be substantially clothed in blankets
of the most valueless tree of all, lodgepole pine. Cleverer
planting practices since the Second World War could have
avoided widespread damage to our freshwater fisheries.
This is not the place to anticipate future forestry policy,
particularly as timber prices are at a fifty-year low and there
seems to be no plausible reason ever to grow a tree for

profit again – unless it is one which takes more than a lifetime to grow (good oak has held its value without trouble). What seems clear is that novel tree-growing techniques in the southern hemisphere (Australia and southern USA) involving forced hardwoods, capable of achieving phenomenal growth rates in warm temperature, have the potential to upset the conventional world timber trade equilibrium. In the British context it seems likely that the extreme reaction to blanket conifer forestry will be redressed before long. Solidly-grounded, non-ideological production of quality timber on appropriate sites, along with proper environmental constraints and mitigations, will have a place when the construction industry recovers. Strategic considerations will come into play as movement of goods around the world becomes costlier. Britain is not a bad place for growing straight and strong trees; it is a good bet that having them will be worthwhile in time.

I have predicted the expansion/contraction prospects for sheep farming and forestry as they affect deer as I see them. The official position on these land uses deserves mention too. Hill sheep farming looks vulnerable, not to any particular animosity from government, but a seeming incomprehension about its real-life economics. When in December 1992 the Minister for Agriculture reduced hill livestock compensatory allowances for sheep farmers he laid down a marker; if the government was looking for savings in its agricultural support budget sheep-men would take the punishment first. An attractive consideration here was that they are not a political force in farming; compared to grain and dairy farmers they have no clout. Twenty million pounds could be saved without too much fuss. The fact that lamb is one of the few products not in surplus in Europe was an irrelevance. The hill farmers in the Highlands, bored until weary with government exhortations to diversify, something they are peculiarly unsuited to, are facing a very bleak future indeed. For reasons of political convenience the true plight of hill farmers' incomes is ignored or blatantly distorted. When the compensatory allowances were reduced the Minister was quick to claim that because of other incidental factors, such as a more favourable green pound rate, hill farm incomes were rising. This statement was received with utter incredulity by those supposed to be enjoying more money. When EC supports go it is difficult in the extreme to see any meaningful replacement income. Mrs Thatcher pledged to keep hill farmers in the hills; the present government has not. So the range for red deer may well expand over the short term.

The official position with forestry has become de-linked from real actions on the ground. The official planting target remains 33,000 hectares a year for all Britain. This is being so underachieved that if anyone thought forestry of much importance it would be an embarrassment. The truth is that the level of subsidy is so high in establishing plantations that there is little likelihood of a change of official policy until the nation's economy markedly recovers. In the meantime there have been many small planting possibilities established under the Woodland Grant Schemes and their associated programmes. These are excellent schemes, committed to beautifying the countryside, using pockets of lazy land, and removing from agricultural production ground growing surplus food. Their level of support balances nicely the costs of doing environmental forestry with diversifying habitat. However, as the sharply sliding scale of grant shows, they are primarily designed for modest planting operations. They do not, and are not intended, to refer to building up a stock of useful timber, reducing the timber import bill, or make a meaningful economic contribution. Whilst little planting is occurring on red deer range at the moment the desirability of more planting, virtually anywhere anybody can be persuaded to undertake it, is a message powerfully issuing from planners. Indicative forestry strategies drawn up by councils comfortably allow for a large increase in the planted area in many Highland situations. Regional planning does not, and never has, taken any account of sporting interests when planning on the large drawing-board. Public officials in Britain are in the Dark Ages about the environmental and economic role of sport; it is seen by planners as an erratic activity, pursued by the few, to be squeezed into corners of the grand plan not used by other more respectable activities. An economic upturn would see considerable increases in incentives to plant as national policy. How these would fit in with the perceived profitability of forestry, with an end-product forty years away, will depend on developments in other countries meantime. Open deer range in the long term has every likelihood of further contraction from forestry.

The last land-use which impinged heavily on open deer range from the 1950s to the 1970s was the flooding of valley-bottoms and straths for hydro-power. This took a considerable acreage away from deer, acreage over which fish protein replaced meat protein. Large-scale hydro-schemes are unlikely ever again to close off glens and passes. There is too much focus on preserving the environment, and a sense that the resource of wild land is both precious and limited in extent. Hydro-schemes have not had their day; they will provide remote communities with power increasingly. But the scale will be small and localized, and have no impact for deer.

The last land-use affecting deer range is the one that occupies, frequently, the same ground – grouse-moors. The relationship between grouse-moors and deer forests has changed in recent time. Much of the deer population problem in the east Grampians is precisely because red deer have moved onto grouse-moors and become hefted there. Like most populations of mammals, including man, red deer are natural colonists, and will expand their range where they can. They are now pushing at the frontiers of conventional range, and have crossed it in places. The RDC would like to constrain them from expanding further by sharply reducing their numbers on the range-fringes. Red deer are now all over Argyll and Cowal in the west, down to the Lake of Menteith in central Scotland, and pushing down the Angus glens and onto the Carse of Gowrie in the east. Much of the ground from which they have launched these incursions was formerly devoted to grouse-moor use. Often the grouse keepers, unused to dealing with large numbers of deer, saw the seriousness of the situation too slowly. Culling did not take place when it should have. This may happen again, not on grouse-moors but on agricultural land fringed with forestry on the present edge of red deer range. If large-scale tree-planting takes place on arable land under Set Aside regimes and farm forestry schemes, red deer will soon be flourishing in congenial new habitats. We have seen this even more pronouncedly in a movement going the other way, from south to north, with roe deer in evergreen forestry. What happens to grouse-moors profoundly affects red deer.

The grouse-moor range has gradually contracted. One way this has happened is that described above – the colonization of grouse-moors by red deer looking for fresh pasture; the other is the slow strangulation of moors which lack the high level of management proper grouse-moors demand. Good shooting moors go back, bags are leaner and leaner, and finally the resources and determination needed to restore them are too overwhelming to mount. The productivity of a grouse-moor depends to an unusual extent on the personality and professionalism of the game-keeper and his boss. Without commitment from both the shooting will decline. There is no hands-off way of running a grouse-moor, and fortunately Scotland can show many fine examples of dedicated management which have produced the goods. For run-down grouse-moors can be resuscitated. Ian McCall of the Game Conservancy gave me an interesting example of the impacts of the ambitions of motivated managers. A Perthshire hill some years back was classed as a good stag forest. The owners died and a keen shooting man took over and put on three gamekeepers. The grouse bag soared up to around 800 brace annually. The grouse-shooting laird was killed in the Second World War, and the post-war emphasis reverted to deer. Stories like these can be run the other way round. But the name of the grouse game – intensive management – favours in the long term the majority of deer/grouse borderline moors going the way of the deer. Grouse-moors are cyclical, expensive to manage compared to deer forests, and they do not unfailingly produce the goods even when treated to textbook management.

The single most intractable factor affecting them is that full protection for all raptors, regardless of densities, will probably defeat even the best efforts of the best keepers. Working with raptors, the methodology being employed at the moment, involves getting sufficient grouse on the ground to allow raptors a free hand scooping them off, then using the surplus for sport. It is exceedingly unlikely that when the grouse population falls really low any moor can in the long term sustain heavy predation from raptors. Both from practical and economic standpoints the poorly-stocked grouse-moor, hosting large numbers of raptors appears, at present states of knowledge, to be doomed. This is a sad scenario. However, this is not the place to discuss whether or not the only economic management of moorland specifically for heather and heather-centred habitat should itself receive protection. The effect of diminishing grouse-moor is that more range has become available for red deer, and more will become available.

There is a further concern about red deer on grouse-moors, that of their interaction with grouse. On moors where grouse numbers have spectacularly crashed the presence of deer has sometimes been blamed. History shows this is manifestly not justified, although deer densities are not without certain impacts. Earlier this century when grouse-moors in the Highlands were often strikingly productive, population cycles were dramatically pronounced. Grouse populations rocketed from the bottom to the top over periods of a few years. Many game-books record this. At the time deer numbers were very thin. I have studied the game-books here at Borrobol from over a hundred years back, when 2000 brace was not an unusual grouse-bag; two years later the annual return was one and a half brace, then back to a thousand in the blink of an eye. The deer cull was tiny and the Edwardians record their delight at even seeing a stag; now I am delighted to see a grouse! In obvious ways deer on grouse-moors do have effects. The biggest one is physical. If the heather is in poor shape heavy grazing by deer can push it lower, and in extreme cases eradicate it. Where deer are too numerous they have the capacity to alter the herbage balance, and bring about the suppression of heather by competition from nutritive fescues and fine bent grasses. If heather-burning policies are incompetent burnt-off heather can succumb to replacement by grasses. The disappearance of heather will tell against the grouse. Generally, however, herbivores perform a useful service on grouse moors by keeping heather-height in check. The two species are fundamentally compatible, and there are many examples of it, but again, management must be watchful and numbers of deer must be controlled. The ultimate impact of deer on grouse is when they eat them. Strange admittedly, but not fiction. Red deer blundering into a grouse-nest have been known to slurp up the handy snack. Scientists on Rhum were astonished to discover that red deer were engorging young shearwaters, or more precisely biting their heads off. Closer study showed that the deer were also stripping the flesh of shearwater bones and chewing the skeletons. What especially surprised the scientist R.W. Furness, reporting in the *Journal of Zoology*, was that the deer had learnt to extract only that part of the corpse that contained the minerals they needed, the bones. A book written in 1905 even attributed the deterioration of grouse-moors to deer eating young grouse. The degree to which herbivores, including sheep and cattle, eat birds has never been fully recognized, but as herbivore populations in the mineral-deficient Highlands are being subjected to increasingly rigorous study, these curious facts are coming to light. How much more interdependent are our numerically-impoverished Highland ecosystems than we ever thought!

# Chapter 4

Questioning of ecological balances has triggered the debate about Highland land-use, which has narrowed into a question about the long-term future of Scotland's red deer. Debates about Highland land-use are a perennial issue, an issue given sharper focus, and the more open to political bias, because of the history of the most contentious issue in recent time, the Clearances. Behind the widespread sentiment of anti-landlordism is this event, deliberately confused for populist purposes with the advent of sporting estates, when in truth the glens were cleared for sheep. Because the most vehement critics of the deer population have turned for an ideal in Highland land-use to the distant past, it is important to trace what has happened over time to the land that deer now tread. This is essentially the history of forest cover, for only parts of northern Sutherland and Caithness, and the Western Isles, escaped colonization by trees after the last Ice Age.

Thirty thousand years ago Scotland was warmer and wetter, and in the open parkland grazed animals we know only from their buried bones, or present-day populations elsewhere. These included woolly mammoth, woolly rhinoceros and reindeer. The ice-cap that froze over this landscape was more than a mile thick. When the ice retreated it left the glacial soils which form the basis of Scotland's present soil cover. Arctic lemmings, giant fallow deer, elk and reindeer now trod the ground. The

*A hind feeding on seaweed during the winter.* (Fiona Guinness)

*A stag who has recently cast his antlers initiates boxing with an antlered stag.* (Fiona Guinness)

*Here a cast stag is forced onto his hind legs by an antlered one who is trying to gain dominance. Stags re-establish their hierarchial positions after casting.* (Fiona Guinness)

*A stag who is beginning to clean his antlers.* (Fiona Guinness)

*A hind suckling and grooming her calf.* (Fiona Guinness)

*Fighting stags.* (Fiona Guinness)

*Deer lying on the beach during the summer. They do this to avoid the flies. The stags are lying apart from each other and this is a way to tell stags from hinds at a distance. (Fiona Guinness)*

*A stag establishing his position in the early part of the rut in a favoured short greens area where hinds prefer to graze. He still has a large belly but will become slim and ready to fight within the following week. Note that the only trees that are able to survive in these conditions are ones such as this rowan tree which is growing from a crevice in a rock. (Fiona Guinness)*

*A stag in his rutting territory marking a post with his antlers.* (Fiona Guinness)

*A stag roaring. He is in full rut and is well slimmed down.* (Fiona Guinness)

*An old stag avoiding the turmoil of the rut by lying on the beach. Note the dried velvet which is still hanging from his antler. (Fiona Guinness)*

*A rutting stag with his harem on the short greens favoured by the hinds. (Fiona Guinness)*

*A stag browsing on silver birch.* (Fiona Guinness)

*Deer sometimes feed precariously on cliffs when feeding is short.* (Fiona Guinness)

*An example of lethal bark stripping.*
(Red Deer Commission)

*This spruce shows the effect of
deer browsing.*
(Red Deer Commission)

trees began to form the ancient forest cover in phases, the first of which was birch; hazel, elm, oak, pine, alder and ash followed in that order, the last occurring around 5000 years ago. Man entered this picture, as archaeological evidence stands today, over 8000 years ago, but large-scale man-made effects did not pre-date the arrival of farming; they started 6000 years ago.

The trees began to thin out and eventually disappear over wide areas. What is striking here is that tree-cover moved down the hills; pine, for example, started to retreat from the upper 2000 metres tree-line around 2500 years ago, at the level at which man is least likely to have been involved. Human dwellings of the period were all on lower terrain. One of the explanations for the shrinking of pine is the coincident eruption of the volcano Hekla in Iceland, and the possible air-borne spread of toxic fumes. A.G. Tansley, who wrote the definitive book on British vegetation in 1939, considers that the underlying cause of forest retreat, prior to human agency, was climatic. Three thousand years ago the climate entered the sub-Atlantic period, characterized by wetter and cooler summers. This change was inimical to trees at high altitudes, and favoured the spread of mosses and boggy plants. Sphagnum literally throttled the forests, smothering their trunks and limbs, and eventually formed the peat layer which itself may be showing signs of decay today. During the pluvial period the dominant tree species were an oak/hazel mix in the south, pine in the central and western Highlands, and birch northwards until the trees petered out.

It seems that human impacts accelerated the processes of nature. Lynx, wild boar, beaver, wild horse, brown bear and the auroch died out, or were destroyed as the forest shrank. The wolf followed in the seventeenth century, exterminated by the swiftly-spreading hand of man. The population of humans grew extraordinarily fast in the eighteenth and nineteenth centuries, and with people came their domestic animals; sheep, goats and small black cattle. Sheep have too often taken the exclusive blame for grazing off saplings and tree-growth in this period, conveniently connecting blame to the Lowlands flock-masters involved in the Clearances. In fact roving herds of goats, seen today as more politically-correct animals, and owned by the indigenous Highlanders, probably played as big a part. In between the clearance of the sheep and the expansion of deer forests at the end of the last century there is evidence that native trees did in fact successfully regenerate, if only for a short time. However, most of the forest clearance was complete by 1700, and where the hills were left bare they gradually turned to the heather moorland that they are today.

There is a vocal body of opinion in Scotland at present, represented by a number of different organizations with much in common, which has made it the chief objective of policy to campaign for the restoration of the Highlands to the post-glacial tree-cover. To the left of centre in political terms, on the urban side of the spectrum in membership terms, almost exclusively outside the framework of deer management in Scotland, this assemblage of people has a vision of the Highland scene which is radically changed from today's. They would like to see the scrub birch of the northern Highlands climb back to its former 2000-metre upper limits; alder and willow would clothe the straths with clumps of pine. Spruce, despite having been present in Scotland before the most recent Ice Age, has no part to play in this revisionist landscaping, being too closely associated with unpopular commercial forestry planted in blocks. In the central Highlands native pine would predominate. Grand plans have been devised to restore pine to the Grampians by natural regeneration. Above the pine tree-limits scrub birch could again form a fringe before altitude made tree-life altogether impossible. The other tree species considered 'native' would all have a part to play. It is envisaged that around sixty per cent of Scotland would be tree-covered, with hill-tops, bogs, fens and lochs making up the remainder. Broadly speaking wherever trees could grow, they would be encouraged to do so.

A key word in this new recipe for land management is biodiversity. Biodiversity holds valuable a variety of species, of genetic gene pools, and a mosaic of ecosystems. The tree types would be various both to enhance the environment, and to reduce the risk of forest damage from pests, wind-throw and fire. Mixed woodlands are better able to withstand biological stresses. The new Scottish forest would improve water quality and help control flooding; there would be a gradual restoration of fertility to Scotland's tired and over-exploited soils. Benefits of the ideal forest have been largely expressed in terms of dividends to the community, the forest providing employment, timber for fuel and construction, and a pleasant place in which to roam and relax. It has been seen too as a venue for expeditions gathering fruit and nuts. To achieve this it is recognized that there would have to be substantive changes in the *status quo*, particularly in regard to land-ownership. Large agricultural and sporting estates are seen as redundant and out-of-date, and suited to replacement by more democratically-accountable community structures. The size of the task, refashioning a large part of Britain, is acknowledged in a call for substantial public investment. The scale of this has never been computed, but may be roughly ascertained from the oft-quoted ideal of small-scale farming/forestry village agriculture practised in the Norwegian fjord-valleys. This is underpinned by a lucrative state-supervised salmon fishery, and massive state subsidisation of agriculture resulting in farm prices two to three times as high as those in the European Community, and levels of direct support up to ten times those in our own Less Favoured Areas.

It is admitted that the only examples of ideal forest management visible today are the results of enlightened private initiatives; but it is felt that private ownership on any large scale is incompatible with the forest of the future. As this target vision has become more refined over time, and the practicalities of achieving it have been examined, it has become clear that the principal incompatibility with today's system and the future is the role of deer. Attention has focused on the most manifest aspect of the deer problem, the red deer. The most honest appraisals of the new forest's problems acknowledge that how we manage the red deer is the pivotal issue. Without addressing it trees will not regenerate. 'Manage' in this context is usually a euphemism for 'remove'.

It has to be said that there are many extremely attractive aspects of this vision for the Highlands (in other parts of Scotland its real likelihood of achievement is too remote for serious consideration). Obviously spawned as a rejection of the Forestry Commission's mistaken policies of west Canadian evergreen monocultures, the new ideal, entitled 'Forest of Scotland' by the environmental organization Scottish Wildlife and Countryside Link, attempts to redress many of the imbalances of the past. In almost all its aims there is little to criticize. Problems only start to arise when these aims are projected against the practical measures needed to enact them. It is at this point that Forest of Scotland's anticipation of forest-cover from coast to coast, in a re-created post-glacial terrain, parts ways with the more pragmatic philosophies of those agencies at present vested with power to bring about some rebalancing of the Highland environment. Apart from the Forestry Commission, now divided into two separate agencies, the principal of these is the amalgamation of the former Countryside Commission for Scotland and the Nature Conservancy Council, in a government body called Scottish Natural Heritage (SNH).

SNH, a collection of individuals drawn from different sources, and divided into four regional committees with twelve government-appointed members in each committee, holds within it diverse opinions. But as experience of the practical utilization of its powers strengthens, and understanding grows of the many, often contradictory, demands and needs being made on the Highlands, its perspectives have become refined. It is perhaps best, given the rich variety of opinion within the organization, to look at the point of view of one of the 'long heads', one who thought persistently about the issues, issues which in many contexts come back to our subject matter, the future of the red deer.

One of the most illuminating and eloquent commentators is the chairman of the north-west SNH region, Sir John Lister-Kaye, who lives close to Beauly in Inverness-shire. Sir John is a scientist, a former self-declared blood-hungry sportsman, a landowner himself, and the manager of a charitable business taking foreign visitors into the wilds to look at Scotland's wildlife and biology. He is a captivating public speaker and has been touring the Highlands beating a particular drum. In essence his historical outline of the Highlands history is conventional. In addition he sees the eighteenth-century population build-up as having great significance. He points to the huge manpower effort in the pre-Clearances clachans in refertilizing vast areas of Scotland, toiling by the sweat of their collective brow, with dung, seaweed, even human manure, to improve pasture. On the basis of Victorian game-bags a century later, Sir John believes there was a colossal biological richness in the Highlands, reaching a climax in the period 1850–1900. Woodcock, snipe, duck, blackgame, were all shot in prodigious numbers. In common with many ecologists he sees biological diversity as having fallen, and continuing to fall, from that peak ever since. Like many arguing his theme he quotes the Scandinavian parallel, citing, in a similar boreal zone, the larger number of plant varieties (in rule-of-thumb terms, thirty plants per square metre quadrant compared to Scotland's eleven). He points to the poignancy of the solitary dog-rose, or wild rose, native species both, now visible only inside the crofter's deer-fenced garden, once spread all over the country. He says that we are sliding dangerously out of ecological balance with open moorland habitat; and that recent deer forest policies of keeping a large stock of hinds so that they will attract in stags during the stalking season is a nonsense. He believes deer numbers should be trimmed to levels the herbage can support, in a reasonable time-frame. He thinks the conservation organizations which demanded, and demand, big and instant reductions in deer numbers, have 'pitched in too hard'. The woodland cover he would like to see, for all the same reasons as others, amounts to no more than ten to fifteen per cent of the Highlands, a very different picture from that promised by the Forest of Scotland. Above all, in con-tradistinction to many pop ecologists, Sir John looks ahead. What about deer after broadleaf tree-cover has become established again? He sees deer moving back into woodland, acting as the 'pruning mechanism', shaping and spacing the forest. Sheltered from climatic rigours they would be bigger deer, capable of attracting high fee-paying hunters, and revitalizing the ever-stressed economics of the glens.

It is a tantalizing vision, developed in a mind that is looking, unlike many, from the inside of the Highland scene outwards, not the reverse. One of my own reser-vations about his critique of the present situation is that the theory of degraded habitat and impoverished landscape has been radically overdone. By fencing off parcels of ground, even in the most unpromising and hostile situation, I have found astonishing quantities and varieties of wildflowers, plants, and consequently insects and birds, miraculously reappearing. Tree saplings, given protection from the grazing beasts, surface abundantly. I broached this with him and he told me about an experiment he has been doing for fifteen years on restoring a small area of former moorland, achieving just these results. In a woodland regeneration scheme in Caithness plants which had not been seen for over 200 years poked their shoots through the mosses. Clearly degradation has not been carried as far as feared. The degraded landscape of the scaremongers is actually a landscape rich in variety but sparing in parading its assets, in which many plant species types are in hibernation, their seeds stored safely below ground.

The same exaggeration has afflicted perceptions of Scotland's native woodlands. These are routinely presented as having been virtually wiped out, victims of the steady destructive mowing by sheep and deer. The fact that natural regeneration is occurring all over the Highlands in many different situations is unrecognized. The falsities of the doomsday claims have escaped criticism because it is necessary to look hard and deep to uncover them. My suspicions were aroused from old landscape paintings of Scotland and studying the forest cover. One landscape painting which comes to mind is of Loch Lomond's west bank in the early nineteenth century. It is portrayed virtually denuded of trees. Now the same scene is of an oak-clad lochside, the oak-cover stretching for nearly twenty miles. The Duke of Sutherland published a sale catalogue of his Sutherland properties in 1905 complete with photographs of the lodges. Running an eye over these it is striking how bare and bleak were the environs. The houses had been recently built; trees had not had time to grow around them. Now the majority of them have woods round about, usually a mix of hard- and softwood trees. The truth probably is that the beginning of the twentieth century was the most tree-denuded time of all. One of the reasons for natural regeneration occurring on open hills today is that stock farming has been intensified and more animals are housed in winter than twenty years ago. Additionally hirsels are walking off the hill permanently, put to market as farm fortunes continue to slide. Not all of this ground has been immediately colonized by deer, and poaching, particularly from the road, has played a part in restoring a diverse landscape. Deer do not graze efficiently along a road from which bullets keep winging towards them.

A misty romanticism about the Highlands of a preferred past appears sometimes to have obscured from view the Highlands of the present. We all admire and appreciate the little pockets of native woodlands, found usually on islands in lochs where deer and sheep have never reached. I can recall a tremendous peacefulness and tranquility tucked away under the canopy of hazel and birch on some of these havens of unrestricted natural growth, oases of verdant profusion in a harsh landscape of wind-blasted desolation. Desolation? Perhaps not. Perhaps the sheer openness stirs some residual human longing for simple shelter, or concealment. The wealth of life in the desolation is impressive, if unearthed. Take birdlife. On my deer forest at Borrobol, an ordinary enough slice of east Sutherland flow ground, we have amassed a bird list of over a hundred species, nearly all spring and autumn visitors. This has been done over five years by qualified guides taking visiting bird-watchers over four different habitats – moorland, conifer forestry, deciduous woodland, and river and loch. Many of these species – golden eagle, hen harrier, merlin, black-throated diver, greenshank, dunlin, crossbill, goshawk – are rare and precious within the European context. Birds are an excellent indicator of general biological diversity because they reflect the

quantities of insect, mammal and plant life. I am no ento-
mologist, nor has any insect study ever been done here,
but a botanist during one six-hour walk discovered just
under a hundred flowering plants and ferns on
Borrobol's open hill alone. There are nature reserves in
Britain which would be delighted to sport so many bird
and plant species. Yet the ground also boasts those hated
herbivores, sheep and deer, wintering something in the
region of 1300 of each. Of other keynote mammals,
wildcat, pine marten, otter and badger are resident,
along with three species of bat. If the place is degraded
to despair, what are all these manifestations of life doing
here? Broaching this question with conservationists I
have never had a satisfactory answer. So before we
embark on a costly re-profiling of the Highlands, that
will put the rural agenda in the hands of professional
academic theorists at the expense of native Highlanders'
jobs; and which has all the appearance of having been
drummed up by a small clique of conservationists; and
which has never been embraced or supported or
espoused by the public at large, these questions need
answering.

There is another reason why the charge of degradation
lacks conviction. The blame is put squarely at the feet of
grazing animals. This ignores the great latent influence on
Highland habitat of climate. Warm dry summers suit the
spread of heather; heather, often reverently spoken of as
natural cover, is itself a colonist, exploiting favourable
conditions after trees had departed the scene, which in
turn happened for partially climatic reasons. For the dem-
agogues of change the climatic causal factors have one
basic disadvantage: they cannot be blamed on anyone.
Insects do not make a handy whipping-boy either. Yet it
is perfectly clear that one of the great influences on
heather health and vitality is heather-beetle. I remember
a summer in the early 1980s when heather-beetles floated

out of the sky in clouds. They were so thick in the air that when I was fishing on the river they came and coated the line, little brown bugs all up and down it. Such numbers had not been seen in living memory. Predictions about their predations on the heather, which they kill in the flower, were gloomy. Sure enough large areas of heather began to turn brown, then grey. No life appeared left. We were wrong. Within two years only a few dead, white patches remained; growth had sprung from the bottom of the plant's stems or from dormant seed. This tale does not alter the fundamentals. The attack had the potential to wipe out a huge area of heather moorland, which would then have put tremendous pressure on the surviving grazing. Conservationists maintained an eerie silence about heather-beetle.

As they are doing now about rabbits. Rabbits are changing the Highlands. They are starting to colonize far-out areas of ground where they never were before. An example of this is in the east Grampians. The secretary of the deer management group there told me rabbits were entrenched at 3000 feet and above. He considered that rabbits were a greater threat to habitat than deer. Rabbits have the power with intensive, low-down cropping of grasses to spread certain grass communities. They can eliminate useful nitrogen-fixing clovers and convert ling heathland to grass. They can alter habitat in localized areas, and break up the ground. Rabbits have almost ceased being a sport species as the fashion for shooting ground game has waned, although it was for sport the Normans first introduced them. I have an inkling that it is this that has saved them from the conservationists' ire. One might imagine that an animal with such a devastating effect on vegetation, which has cost the countryside unquantifiable sums in ring-barked young trees and in crop losses, with its fearsome potential for self-replication, would arouse concern with the officials in charge of nature. They, however, airily dismiss the rabbit from their field of view; as it is a non-native (actually it was present before, but in between the ice ages) the former nature conservancies have no formal position on the subject.

One of the themes most commonly referred to in the rejuvenation of Highlands habitat is that of native species. A casual impression of the land-use debate would suggest that conservation bodies were minded above all to promote native species at the expense of introduced ones. At the most extreme there are calls for the reintroduction of the wolf, a concept imported from America. The first wolf reintroduction in the Midwest was calculated to have cost ten million dollars per wolf pair, the money being spent on compensation to farmers, and preparing habitats suitable for the animal. The 'natives only' argument refers to deer in two ways, in deer species themselves, and regarding their habitat. I recall visiting the central Highlands estate of Abernethy where the Royal Society for the Protection of Birds is trying to restore those best-credentials native species: capercaillie (actually reintroduced) and Scots pine. The Scots pine was coming back after heavy culling of red deer, but progress was slow. Little saplings sprouted in clumps mostly on the roadside. In a strath-bottom I spied another clump, of good young trees about fifteen years old. When I commented favourably on this the reserve manager told me, No, this clump was actually being rooted out; the reason – its genotype was non-native. The foreigner was going to be turfed out! The point of view seemed extreme, precious, academic. How many RSPB members, in whose name and with whose money the programme was being financed, would have been able to tell the difference or would have minded if they had? The point about the nativeness of species is important because it is central to the argument about the future of deer and the way we manage their range. Is the native species distinction useful? Or do we risk, in

espousing an emotionally appealing concept of individu-
ality in our island biotypes, embracing a policy of the
absurd?

Painfully absent from the debate about red deer, with
its blue-chip native species lineage, has been discussion
about the non-native deer species, sika. Sika interbreed
in some circumstances with reds, which puts at risk the
purity of our red deer bloodlines; they are particularly
pernicious destroyers of forestry; they are spreading
alarmingly fast in Scotland; they are notoriously secretive
and hard to control; and they hail from east Asia. Yet
whereas we are prepared to countenance the uprooting
of non-native sub-species of Scots pine, no mention is
made of controlling an active, ranging, destructive
colonist. The problem with the omission from the land-
use debate of sika is that it confirms what many deer
managers suspected – the conservationists' call for a
sharp reduction in deer numbers is motivated by, at best,
habitat concerns, not deer concerns. The arguments
advanced by those in favour of the Forest of Scotland,
that fewer deer, a landscape in which deer have a token
presence, will produce better stag trophies for foreign
sportsmen, is revealed as a habitat-orientated viewpoint
parading as a deer-orientated one. The aim of producing
fewer but better stags, to be shot Continental-style from
static positions in high seats, is a red herring meant to
assuage the fears of sporting managers.

The question of nativeness is in any case a vexed one,
and one in which the definitions are elastic. Fallow deer,
Britain's most widespread deer species, is an introduced
species to Britain – officially. But fallow deer were
present in Britain during three pre-glacial geological
periods – as far as we know. Native, with a long pre-
glacial pedigree, or non-native? Recently radio-carbon
dating of a wood-mouse, a species thought to have been
brought along with the Vikings, has shown that, at any

rate in Ireland, it was with us 7600 years ago. The wood-mice on the northern Scottish isles, and Outer and Inner Hebrides are definitely of Norwegian stock. Should they be rooted out, as a precursor to reintroductions of the earlier type? Cloud-cuckoo-land? Not entirely. The entire forestry policy being developed by British conservation organizations is divided along native/non-native lines.

For example, the status of the sycamore is presently subject to re-examination. Formerly cast into outer darkness as a Norman introduction it is now thought that, like the wood-mouse, it may have been here for a long while. In this strange world of 'ethnic cleansing' we risk casting out a species thought to be impure, to discover later its origins are alright. The whole ideology of native species only can have profound and lasting conse-quences for land managers trying to create habitats and simultaneously look after the mammals which depend on them. Sycamore and beech are not welcome components of Woodland Grant Schemes. For a land manager in the central Highlands trying to regenerate Scots pine there are huge differences between grant levels for native and non-native stocks. If the existing parent trees are of unknown origin the higher level of grant is unavailable. No-one could tell the difference, peering up at the tree-crown waving over their heads; detection requires labo-ratory analysis. The natives-only pogrom has led Highland Regional Council down the avenue of objecting to forestry proposals which are ethnically impure. In cul-tivation terms, fertilizer inputs, the genetic stock used, and the demand for varied stocking rates which create problems for final timber extraction, landowners are being obliged to plant or regenerate trees in a manner that throws to the wind our hard-earned seventy years of experience in growing commercial timber.

We may appear to have strayed away from the matter of red deer. This is not the case; habitat and the fauna and flora that dwell in it are inseparable. The species of trees that are planted affect deer, in general and also in specific ways. Deer especially like browsing alder and willow; they favour attacking lodgepole first in a mix of conifers; when short of certain minerals they will ring-bark trees, when adequately supplied with those minerals they will not; deer will attack everything vegetal which is sited on certain soil-types because the plants draw up from the ground minerals they want. Forestry design, physical and in terms of species selection, is central to deer management and is only separated from it at cost. In some of our forestry plantations, established with enormous quantities of taxpayers' money, the end-crop has been 95 per cent damaged by deer. The cost of deer damage to British timber-product has never been computed. It runs into millions of pounds. Therefore a forestry strategy which is not also a strategy for managing deer is a short-sighted folly. Forestry policies and deer management policies should be planned in tandem. This is being done in the biggest area of woodland in Scotland, in the Borders at Eskdalemuir.

Booker Countryside's wildlife manager at Eskdalemuir is a deer-man to the toes of his sprung-soled boots. His father and grandfather were stalkers to the royal family at Balmoral, and he has worked with deer all his life. At one stage in his career he worked as a roving deer controller and covering all Scotland removed 5000 deer on his own account. He is responsible for a deer cull of 2000 beasts a year on fifty-seven Borders properties, constituting the heaviest deer-populated ground in Scotland. I first encountered him at a roe stalking course at Faskally, Perthshire, which he presented to a collection of teenage would-be stalkers with startling fervour and flavour. His name is Ronnie Rose, he has earned an MBE, and no one looking at deer in Scotland can ignore his experience and track-record. If we want to learn how to plant trees which will make timber, his guidelines on wildlife management in the woodlands repay study. The same is true if we want to learn to live with deer.

Deer management, in his view, starts with forest design. Deer have to be controlled in forestry, unless we don't care a hoot about the end-crop, and to control them you must first see them. Ronnie Rose thinks we have a legacy to cope with of forty years of bad forest design. Trees were planted in blocks that stretched as far as the eye could see. When he first suggested leaving 5 per cent of the plantable area for deer control he was told how much timber revenue was being sacrificed. Plants and their habitat being the same subject, it does not work like that. It is the trees that are being sacrificed. Bark-stripping leads to fungal growth which stains the wood rendering it useless even for pulping. Bark-stripping weakens the bole of the tree which becomes prone to snapping, even in mild winds. It crashes down injuring neighbouring trees, sometimes writing them off. The first thing Ronnie Rose mentions when touring the counry to speak about his methods is that his prime aim is to protect trees until they are harvested for commercial use. So, bark-stripping has to be minimized.

Forest design, in his book, starts with natural features. Deciduous trees are useful buffers for protecting the commercial investment and supporting wildlife generally; special tree species can be planted to minimize damage to the core-crop. Steep slopes beside rivers, frost hollows facing east and south, the tops of hills and rocky outcrops on hillsides, are obvious areas to be left unplanted.

Where red deer are expected to get in, as opposed to roe deer, the spaces should be bigger. Their needs must be allowed for. This means leaving open also areas where the soil types are right, providing deer with the summer grasses (mostly fescues) they need, and leaving unplanted the heathery banks they use in winter. Ronnie Rose takes this as far as saying all forestry design should use a soil map at planning stages. His principle is to get the deer into the areas where you can control their numbers. Deer lawns will facilitate this. Roadside culling, by contrast, has the undesirable effect of making the animals nocturnal, which compromises culling. He has noted along roads from which deer have been potted at, the bark on the forest side chewed, the bark on the road side of the same tree untouched. He disapproves of night-shooting on humanitarian grounds, and because it is ineffective and unselective. Up to 15 per cent of the forest should be left open for deer management purposes. He sees a sitka spruce plantation as an inherently artificial man-made creation, and therefore the necessity to mitigate its artificiality for the benefit of wildlife as a whole. The presence of short-eared owls, amongst other birds, is specially encouraged because of their fondness for the tree-pests, short-tailed voles. When some forest owls were spending too much time eating these voles, whilst some neighbouring water voles were threatening the construction nearby of an earth-dam, he got the owls to alter their diet by moving a fence-post, which the owls were using for observation, step by step, in the direction of the water voles. Finally pellet samples showed the owls had switched diet as wanted. A small example of Ronnie Rose's holistic approach to wildlife management.

The basis of his approach to a new control problem is observation first, then analysis. The female is the focal point of the cull. The stags are attracted to her in the rut and can be shot. She must therefore not be harassed or forced to dodge around. The number of females can be controlled in the winter. He believes we should use our knowledge of soil types to cater for deer in forestry and pull them into lushly grassy areas where control can be exercised. Deer and forestry are, to Ronnie Rose, insepararable management issues.

The specialization of his approach means that special-
ists are required in order to pursue the right ends. He
believes the Scottish stalking profession is three times too
small for the job. He is particularly disparaging about the
use of volunteer stalkers in place of pro's, 'part-time
gunners coming from anywhere' he calls them. He
laments the vogue in private forestry companies of letting
stalking commercially in the expectation that the visiting
rifle will adequately perform a proper control operation
at the same time. It never happens. The stalking tenant
comes from afar, wants to bag a trophy male or two, and
is disinclined to sweat out the rough wintry days doing
the key thing, knocking out the females. The tenant, in
the Rose book, cannot replace the manager. What
happens when this is attempted is that the small stalking
rents realized in the short term are offset in the long one
by serious damage to the woodlands. The visiting stalker
will patrol the forest-edge waiting for opportunities to
pop up. In the meantime inside the spruce thicket havoc
is being wreaked unseen. Ronnie Rose says that sadly the
proportion of forests in Scotland shot unsupervised has
risen to 70 per cent. The Europeans, who he believes are
light years ahead of us in their management of woodland
deer, find it difficult to credit that we run our affairs this
way. In Germany, for example, two or three men are
deployed to manage the wildlife on only 500 hectares;
here we normally have one man on twelve times that
area. He deplores the encouragement of night-shooting
(state forestry stalkers get overtime for night-shooting),
again outlawed in Europe, arguing that it encourages
bark-stripping as the deer doesn't dare feed any more in
the open. He thinks we should go down the European
path and train our forestry workers in ecology, a subject
virtually absent from our forestry training courses, and
which constitutes three-quarters of training on the
Continent.

As you might expect he is not short of commentaty on the latest ideas in forest design *vis-à-vis* natural regeneration. Trying to do this without fencing is, in his view, absurd, like 'making a circle in the sea and trying to stop the water coming in'. Looking past the objectives of achieving the thicket stage with naturally regenerated forest he points out that, if not fenced out, the deer will disappear back into the middle again. To control them once more will require man-made interventions, areas in which they can be controlled, which will look far from natural. The whole concept he dismisses as emanating from 'the ninnies in green knickers'. The views of Ronnie Rose, probably the most experienced and knowledgeable woodland deer manager in Scotland, are not fashionable. Armchair land-use experts do not want to be told they lack practical experience; forestry managers do not like being accused of short-sighted cost-cutting; no one likes hearing that our management of woods and deer is grotesquely incompetent. But when Ronnie Rose is saying it, whilst presiding over the most densely-shot woodland stalking in Britain, on top-range commercial forestry, it behoves serious participants in the debate to listen.

The reason for what may seem an alarming degree of disharmony about Highland land-use is thoroughly complex. There are causes which are historical and social, and there are causes which derive from the gulf, more pronounced in Britain than comparable countries, between country-dwellers, those born with earth under their finger-nails, and urban viewpoints. We are a more populous country than most others in Europe, and a smaller percentage of us live on the land. As the Common Agricultural Policy disputes have shown, the land-links forged in the minds of many Europeans are stronger than ours. In place of countrymen and women we have a plethora of people trained to look at the land as an academic exercise. People with doctorates in subjects ranging from liverworts to lichens are legion. It is the mixing and matching of these disciplines within a financial framework, something which can best be understood by practical involvement, that is missing. This was painfully clear in the 1980s when the Nature Conservancy Council for Scotland managed, with its precious, tunnel-vision perspectives on the designation of Sites of Special Scientific Interest, to alienate among others the entire farming community in the county of Caithness. It often seemed to the ordinary farmer, crofter or landowner that within the conservancy one hand did not know what the other was doing. The peat-bog specialist would arrive in nesting-time to trample over a site just described as vital for rare nesting birds. And so on. The legacy is still there in the new body, Scottish Natural Heritage, and it is proving hard to overcome. The problem in Britain is simpler to state – we lack overall co-operation between land-uses – than to overcome.

The best demonstration of this is the report, published in March 1993, of the Cairngorms Working Party. It is a highly important document, both because its recommendations cover a large part of the central Highlands, constituting the area that is popularly thought of as archetypal Highland landscape, and because some of the advisory scientists casually mention that the prescriptions for deer management (or proscriptions against deer) could be applied over the rest of deer range equally well.

In essence the report appears to give precedence to conservationists' passion for the re-creation of the ancient Caledonian Forest at the expense of red deer. Those invited to advise the working party on deer and woodland management, who appear to be for once in line with each other, would argue that the social and economic well-being of the area also has been sacrificed on the altar of tree regeneration.

In the wake of the government's refusal to institute national parks for Scotland, and after heated debate even at Parliamentary level about the future of one of the Cairngorm area's most important estates, Mar Lodge, the Secretary of State for Scotland set up the Cairngorms Working Party in March 1991. The brief was to study the issues affecting the Cairngorms, including the natural heritage and resources, land-use practices, recreational demands, and the needs and aspirations of the local residents (one local pre-empted this last clause at the outset by saying the aspirations of locals were not to be included in the report – an example perhaps of weariness at the over-designation the area has attracted). The working party was further instructed that the government wanted to see a recommendation based on the voluntary principle. It was asked to ignore financial, ethical and statutory considerations, omissions which can be seen as a possible escape route for a government under pressure to do something. For one thing no-one really doubted at the outset – whatever came out at the end would make demands on the public exchequer. Had the existing structures been capable of meeting everyone's objectives in a free market, the need for the working party would never have arisen.

Agreement on the importance of their own job was the final report's only unanimously supported item. The 180-page document then outlines a strategy for creating two new huge forests, the Forest of Strathspey and the Forest of Mar, the first to the east of Aviemore, the second surrounding Braemar and stretching westwards. The principal idea of these two forests is to be 'semi-natural', with some densely-wooded areas and others of more scattered trees. The 'natives only' policy is to be enforced, to the extent that aliens like larch, lodgepole and spruce, along with pine of nineteenth-century German extraction, shall be felled, if necessary prematurely, and replaced with respectable British trees. How is this to be achieved, given that at present, and in fact for hundreds of years, deer have been known to suppress natural regeneration in the Cairngorms, especially in winter when the stags take cover under the trees? The answer – without fencing – a method certain to be the key point of contention as the report goes out to consultation, and in the event of any future enactment of the policy. Furthermore the new forests are to spread onto existing moorland, where the deer spend some of their summer.

Where do the deer come in? They are to go out – in the game-dealer's van. Most of them anyway. The report is coy about what level of culling would be required to achieve its aims, although it points out that on nearby moorland deer stocking rates need not be reduced so hard. It acknowledges that the local deer management groups have successfully culled hinds down towards a reduced population. But the fact it skirts admitting is that the needs of naturally regenerating pine seedlings demand a reduction in deer numbers to population levels which are far too low for sporting managers. In the eighteenth century, when some planting and sowing was attempted in the Cairngorms, the young trees were protected by dykes and ditches. Even when deer populations were low the need for protection of young trees was recognized. For the pine seedling is a feeble beastie. Many of the parent Cairngorms trees are 170 years old, some over 220; seed from them is not potent. Pine seedlings need light, and they compete inefficiently with field-layer plants. This is why in Abernethy the re-seeded saplings are mainly on the roadside, wherever fresh soil has been exposed, and where there is human disturbance to scare off deer. Good seed years are in three- to six-year cycles. It is a slow process. The RDC in its submissions to the working party was adamant – reducing deer numbers low enough for regeneration to occur was unrealistic. The submissions of deer managers echoed this; there was no option but to fence. The East Grampians Deer Management Group, one of the area's participant groups, presently responsible for 13 per cent of the entire recorded red deer cull, aims to reduce deer numbers on its uniquely over-pressurized ground by one-third, bringing about a projected deer density of ten to twelve animals on a hundred hectares. But this group, with its wealth of recent experience in reducing top-heavy deer populations, submitted that to create a deer-free zone on an area of 50,000 hectares, of open hill would require a reduction in numbers over an area ten times that size. This is because of the so-called 'sump effect', whereby deer are sucked in to ungrazed ground by the more succulent feeding it offers. The aims of the project to naturally regenerate the old forest would, without fencing, require a change of management and the removal of deer over an enormous area.

The figures the Cairngorms Working Party skirted, about how many deer would need removing, can be gleaned from experiments done by the former NCC on state-owned conservation projects. One of these is at Creag Meagaidh, a 4000-hectare former deer forest within the Monadhliath deer management group. Sheep, once hefted on Creag Meagaidh, were cut back to tiny numbers. Deer numbers between 1977 and 1990 were reduced by 91 per cent. A deer population numbering nearly 1200 in 1973 had been thinned out to 56 in 1990. This can safely be described as radical change. The manager there is Dick Balharry, one of the most consistent proponents of deer reductions for the benefit of trees, who has gone as far as saying that the real resource (from the ecologist's viewpoint) is the vegetation that grows on deer range, not the deer.

Dick Balharry points to the ground for proof of the success of his management. His team counts the birch saplings growing on the hillside at Creag Meagaidh. Not surprisingly they found saplings sprouting up vigorously as soon as grazing animals had gone, or been radically reduced. Proof, perhaps, that the notorious degradation of habitat is an over-simplification, or a misrepresentation. To achieve the respite from browsing and grazing heavy culling of deer has taken place, supplemented by removal of deer, mostly hinds, in live capture. In the first year of intensive deer reduction efforts 475 animals were removed, 375 by culling. Methods not open to private estates on grounds of cost, such as helicopter collection of carcasses were employed. The policy of deer reduction was open-ended; deer were to continue to be removed until natural regeneration was successful. Heavy culling continued; and deer counts dropped to a token presence. Dick Balharry maintains his policy has been successful in terms of habitat regeneration, and can show that some birds formerly absent have returned to Creag Meagaidh, plus a first-time breeding bird for Britain, the icterine warbler. He believes the improved habitat will manifest itself in healthier deer, a point few people would care to contest. It has been known since big houses kept park deer that their physical measurements were most closely related to diet and the quality of range. Creag Meagaidh will certainly provide a tasty bite. As there is no commercial stalking, and because of the habitat interest, the reserve is able to siphon visitor pressure off neighbouring estates during the culling season. The manager's only rather esoteric belief, against those of ordinary keepers, is that there is no place for heather-burning as a regular moorland management tool. He thinks burning threatens to turn heather to grassland, presumably having taken as his instruction the western Highlands burnt in huge areas for sheep and not the eastern, northern and central Highlands where heather management is important to deer control. As Frank Fraser Darling said, it is not the fact of burning heather that should be disputed, but how it is done. In

Dick Balharry's view old heather should simply be planted with native woodlands; which poses a bleak outlook for heather moorlands which should never be burnt.

Creag Meagaidh was a contentious experiment when it was started in 1986 because neighbours feared their deer would wander into the vacated grazing and get shot too. One estate's whimsicalities were to be put into practice at the expense of its neighbours. Over time these fears have moderated. Dick Balharry tags his deer and watches which deer leave the ground and which come in. He says the movement is not great. Hefted hinds he believes, will stay, by and large, on their hefts. This depends on the behaviour of neighbours. Researchers support his contention that hinds stay remarkably close to their birth place. But the research has taken place in situations where conditions are stable. A sudden disappearance of deer on deer ground is not stable. The Monadhliath Deer Management Group to which Creag Meagaidh belongs found that there had been a 20 per cent drop in deer counted on estates adjacent to the reserve in the years 1987–90, a drop in fact of over 800 animals. Presumably some sump effect was working. It is an absurdity to say deer are invulnerable to the sump effect, proved by the east Angus glens where the fastest build-up of red deer numbers in modern times occurred in the late 1980s on range which was traditionally grouse-moor. Stags are principally the sex that wander, a fact well understood by poachers. It will never be possible to kill out deer in a localized way and expect the gap to remain empty.

Dick Balharry, understandably, is unkeen on the counting and culling technique for determining management. He is reluctant to focus too hard on how many deer have had to be sacrificed for his project. The counting he prefers is of trees. He is a persuasive advocate of regeneration of woodland, and most people would be in sympathy with what has been done at his reserve. But whether they would remain in sympathy with it if the rest of the Highlands was a thicket of young trees is dubious. It has been proved conclusively that, from a scenic viewpoint, the Highlands are loved for their openness and space. One further thing strikes the visitor to Creag Meagaidh – that it has no commercial or working purposes. It rocks gently in the cradle of state support. Recently the value of a stag rented out for sport on a deer forest has been computed, along with the ancillary values of the visiting sportsman to the community, at £700. Creag Meagaidh forgoes this income on every stag that is no longer present there, along with the loss of venison revenue. In the private sector Dick Balharry's role would need a form of sponsorship that is rare. And, of course, as he realizes, before long deer will be hiding up in the thicket. He will face Ronnie Rose's problem. Rides or glades, impolitely called 'killing fields', will need to be carved out. Not only is this an expensive operation (the Forestry Commission have had to do it in some of their woods and the difficulties have been horrendous), but the scenario will no longer be natural at all. If this is not done then the whole process of a population build-up, and the gradual reduction of habitat, will recur. Nature does not stand still. Today's ideal is tomorrow's headache.

This is especially true of trees. What happens at the sapling stage determines the tree that towers over our heads in seventy-five years. If more than a third of the crown of a young tree is bitten off the plant degenerates. The Cairngorms Working Party, abusing its wide remit by selectively focusing on deer and trees, solicited less input from foresters than any other type of professional. This shows up in a tragically imbalanced and impractical pre-scription for tree-growing. The recommendations appear to understand, at any rate partially, that their implemen-tation will drastically cut back stalking. But they show no awareness whatever that they will also fail to produce useful timber. For in the Highlands useful timber has to be managed right through to the productive stage. The Duke of Atholl and the Earl of Seafield understood this when they planted their huge acreages in this part of the Highlands two centuries ago. There is evidence of the timber-growing qualities of the area still splendidly visible today. It is the prime tree-growing location in the Highlands. But these growing trees were protected in the growing phases. I have already mentioned how fragile is the Scots pine seedling. One chomp from the mouth of a hungry stag in winter can remove the lead-shoot. The little tree responds by growing two shoots and a split crown. That chomp has curtailed the tree's commercial usefulness for the rest of its long life.

Fending off that chomp is a long-term exercise. The tree-crown is within reach of a browser up to about six feet from the ground – when the ground is clear. If the frost solidifies a three-foot snowfall it acts as a platform from which the stag can continue filling his stomach. A red deer will continue eating and chewing that tree, if nothing else is on hand, for around thirty-five years depending what growth it has put on. In other parts of Scotland 'attractors' are planted to distract deer from the commercial crop; the working party eschewed these practical steps presumably because they might wander from the self-inflicted holy writ of doing nothing unnatural. Our forefathers would say it beggared belief. Without fencing, some deer, despite the mind-boggling cull that is to occur, will get in and chomp. The working party's avowed intent to look after the economic and social well-being of people who live in the area is in flat contradiction to the politics it recommends which are certain, if effected, to shrink the timber-industry base. Most directly because the trees which would produce the timber that is wanted – larch and spruce – are expressly prohibited from being planted. In the meantime the expansion of forest cover at higher altitudes on heathery moorland, which is not expected to be commercial, will shrink the present land-uses that are commercial: sheep farming, grouse shooting and deer stalking. If today's ideologues were prepared to take a lesson from the successful practitioners of the past, expensive working parties and mounds of verbose paper work could be avoided. In the past forestry enterprises were fenced, so that other land-uses could take place alongside them. But then the working party has subsumed any vestigial interest in multiple land-use within a blind obsession with the regeneration of native pine. Canadian lumberjacks in the last two wars selectively removed from the Caledonian Forest many of its straightest stems; the seed-source of the future regenerated Scots pine will be those left behind as useless, a point seldom remarked, which shows how theoretical aims have dominated practical ones.

The arguments about fencing are critical, and give the flavour of prevailing thinking. A deer fence is said to be expensive. No problem there: people have always been prepared to shoulder that cost for the benefits rendered. A further point: the costs of fencing vary. The routine costings used by public bodies are around double what I pay for deer-fencing using a contractor who is generally agreed to erect a better fence than his rivals. Then a fence is seen to be artificial. Really! We entered the historical phase of enclosure-development a long time ago, in order to discriminate between one land-use and another. On an island pressed for space can we seriously consider dropping back a thousand years and arduously creating a natural space, which will resound to the firing of rifles as the deer are shot out? The contradictions are manifold. Allegedly a fence-line is objectionable because the ground inside and outside looks different. The language here is that the vegetation inside fails to 'mimic' the vegetation outside. The vegetation inside the garden wall does not mimic what is beyond: are we therefore to remove the wall? One submission to the working party even objected to scarification, which is scraping the ground to prepare it for naturally-falling seeds, because ground preparation was artificial. Comment is unnecessary. Another anti-fencing argument: fences have killed birds flying into them, including capercaillie. This should be avoidable. Fences should be planned to be visible. The old-fashioned grouse-moor technique of tying bunches of heather to the top deterred birds; so do plastic streamers criss-crossed over the top wires. Fencing which is not high-tensile but gives when hit by flying objects, bounces birds back off. Normally birds hit fence-lines and power-lines when panicked and being pursued. Landscape design which avoids bird losses from high wires needs looking into. But in the meantime the numbers of birds killed by the railway running through the Cairngorms, and its roads, are a bigger worry than deaths from static obstacles. Old gamekeepers always acknowledged that fences killed grouse, but the effects tailed off as the resident birds got to know the fence-lines. A last objection to fencing was mounted by the Ramblers Association – they blocked access. Have they not heard of stiles?

The working party's recommendations threaten to undermine the essentially fragile economics of the existing land-uses in the Cairngorms. Not only will the forestry policy box landowners and farmers into a plantation-system that fails to maximize the potential of the land, but the crops it envisages will be more expensive to extract. Modern tree-growing practices, unshackled by land-use ideologies, factor-in extraction at the planning stage. Spruce and larch are popular trees for foresters because not only do they grow well but they are not densely foliated low down. Timber fellers charge less to cut spruce than pine. It will be interesting to see the forestry investors' reaction to investment blocks in the new/mediaeval Cairngorms creation.

It is plain that the working party's report has revealed great strains and stresses amongst the various bodies vying for control of the rural agenda in this area. Representations from landowner bodies, articulating also the views of farmers, foresters and crofters, were often indignant at the way the Cairngorms had been turned into an issue by unrelenting media coverage. The traditional residents had been put under the microscope to a degree that had provoked anger. The feeling running through the representations from resident bodies was that their own life-styles were in jeopardy and to be replaced, or put under supervision, by an administration set up from outside and guided by imported ideologies. If the existing social structure is to stay in place, huge increases in public subsidy will be needed to replace the industries that must go. The area will become, potentially, a welfare black hole, disallowed from carrying out productive land-based activities, lacking incentives to be productive, geared increasingly to manage the massive tourist overload which over-designation attracts.

In England the residents of designated national park areas have mounted impressive protest movements, beseeching governments to release them from the special status that have been stuck with. The arrival of the first pro-active conservationist is equated with that of the Grim Reaper himself. I remember researching the use of the lakes for leisure in Cumberland and ringing a female resident who opened the conversation by saying, 'You are ringing Hell'. Erosion, so often blamed on bad land-use, is often caused by human pressure. Our mountains are being ground down by the hill-boot not the hill sheep. But in a democracy the hill-boot needs to be appeased. Often it is the visiting hill-boot rather than the shepherd's that is appeased. The record of locals' involvement with the grand schemes in the Highlands has been poor. When the blanket of lodgepole pine began to crawl over the northern Highlands in the late 1960s the locals were sceptical. The stalking jobs and shepherding jobs they knew and understood were lost. Now, as they always predicted, the forestry jobs are being lost. Forestry employment was dependent on a rolling programme of planting, until the land ran out. Now the jobs have run out. A tiny proportion of the labour force is left. Because, of course, once in the ground, the trees can be left to themselves; particularly when the end-crop is so low-value that protection is uneconomic. The irony is that the only regular income to be had from those huge acreages of bendy trees is from stalking the deer that have invaded. However we twist and turn we end up back with stalking.

There is such antipathy to stalking for sport it is worth asking what we would be doing without it. There is a crucial difference between stalking, and grouse shooting and salmon fishing: stalking is a management necessity, the other two are not. No one yet, even given the bewildering breadth of opinion that gives voice today, has suggested that deer control is completely abandoned – except those who advocate the ultimate in re-created naturalness, reintroduced bears and wolves. Have they any concept of the range-area demanded by a grizzly, or of the effects on bears of becoming habituated to human presence? Presumably not. No, if sport stalking was, heaven forbid, illegalized the job would have to be done by paid professionals. Instead of the private sector employment of stalkers, and revenues gained from sporting visitors, there would be public sector costs. You can be quite sure that whatever costs are met by private estates at the moment would easily become overwhelming if publicly financed. Either that, or the job would not be done. Or the job would be done, but by poachers. A

Swiss canton has taken this path. Pressure from local greens abolished sport hunting. Ten professional hunters were engaged to take over. Paying for this operation, deprived of sport income, bust the canton's finances. Sport stalking was resumed.

Making the sport available for too many people has had disappointing results also. In many American states anyone can buy a hunting licence. In a state like Texas a real man has to drive back into town in the evening with a buck draped over the fender. Nice idea, but bad in practice. Emphatically bad for wildlife management. A free-for-all has resulted in the moose and whitetail deer changing their habits. In heavily hunted areas they cower in the brush and are no longer seen in daylight. They have become crepuscular. Numbers of whitetails have gone on rising; they are now in millions. The big animals have been shot out. There is a dramatic decline in the quality of heads in those areas where there is no private, controlled management. Wounding beasts is common and gung-ho attitudes to wildlife have got the ascendancy. Deer get shot from the back of a truck, often with semi-automatic weapons. Professional hunting guides increasingly have closed their businesses. There is no longer any interest in placing the shot, and an unattractive blending of military and sporting self-identification has developed. As public sector hunting has declined private sector sporting ranches have increased to cope with demand for the properly-managed hunting experience. The deer, or exotic game, is fenced in, and no longer free-ranging. Scotland is unique in Europe in having the open-hill stalking experience to offer. Going down the American road is to be avoided. It would break new records in wastefulness of existing resources.

# Chapter 5

When human beings dispute populations and ecological balances in wild animals, points of view rotate around the question of numbers, numerical assessments. Arguments have become so fraught about the actual numbers of individual species that in some cases teams of scientists have been deployed to provide dispassionate evidence on populations. For example, with regard to seals the government's advisory service on numbers is the Sea Mammals Research Unit. But opinion is so divided, and sometimes so much is at stake, that the objectivity of these scientists is itself questioned. The Sea Mammals Research Unit is accused of suppressing true seal numbers, or massaging figures. Red deer population assessments have been afflicted with these same arguments. Those who wish to emphasize the deer problem say that deer counts underestimate numbers because some deer are hidden in forestry. Deer counting now is performed to try and accommodate this, by pellet-counting in forestry, or by counting the deer in the spring when forest-dwellers are likely to be visible at the edges. The RDC recently tested its own counting system's efficacy by comparing helicopter counts using infra-red with figures obtained from men on the ground; the difference was only 4 over a total of 144. So RDC counts can be assumed to be moderately efficient. The workaday figure for the red deer population in Scotland at the end of 1992 was 300,000, up from about 270,000 in the 1980s.

Reckonings on numbers of deer in times gone by are sheer speculation. All we know from prehistory is that red deer were in Scotland in sufficient numbers to have formed the basic animal resource off which the human population lived. It seems probable that the rapid growth in the human population in the eighteenth and nineteenth centuries owed something at least to a good meat diet of venison. In the early eighteenth century it was commented that the low numbers of deer in likely areas was due to the skill of local hunters and the popularity of venison. The deer herds were pushed uphill again when the flock-masters arrived from the south in the late eighteenth century, and the deer population was squeezed as never before. When deer forests were formed from the huge tracts of land held by hereditary tribal landowners, keepers and stalkers prowled the ground protecting the big deer. But no deer counts were performed. There have always been peaks and troughs in the deer population, caused by climatic factors and hard winters as well as human exploitation. Louis Stewart, the RDC's most highly-regarded old-timer, believes the population peak of the late 1930s was probably similar to today's. A tremendous slaughter took place during and after the Second World War, firstly because the stalkers were called into service as army snipers and desirable meat was trotting around the hills untended, and secondly because in the post-war period many ex-servicemen had rifles and knew how to use them. There was rationing of meat in Britain, and in any case estates were facing an insecure future and much of the land was improperly policed. Both my grandfather and my grandmother spent wartime at Borrobol in Sutherland killing deer to provide meat for a protein-poor, blockaded populace. Venison was so scarce after the war that the price reached three shillings and sixpence old money per pound; by 1950, as the procurement of meat for the nation got under way, it had slumped to a fifth of that.

Winters were quite different during this period. Some have called it a mini Ice Age. In 1947 the west Highlands experienced twelve weeks of solid frost. This must have progressively hardened the ground, presumably freezing it solid to three feet or more. Deer suffered badly and many died. My father recalls travelling from the south in April and counting over a hundred dead stags lying at Kilphedir, only two miles from Helmsdale on Sutherland's east coast. In 1955 'Operation Snowdrop' airlifted provisions to some isolated families in central Sutherland. Dead deer littered the landscape. Calvies die as the weather hits them, but winter deaths among adults occur more in the spring than actually during the freeze-ups; the first flush of green grass is when stags keel over. In spring 1964 the Nature Conservancy counted 400 dead deer in one east Angus glen; extrapolate that figure over all the narrow glens of east Angus and the scale of mortalities from normal causes must have been astonishing. Such scenes of devastation aroused no particular comment in those days. Local people accepted the rigours of winter and the price nature paid; after all it was exacting the same cost from their flocks of sheep. Human mobility was less, and sensibilities less inured to Highland hardship saw little sign of the losses by the time they arrived amidst the purpling heather in August. In this period deer numbers were low, and hard seasons kept them low.

The next black spot in deer deaths from natural causes was in the winter of 1989–90 in the west Highlands. Continual rain and hard winds resulted in many deer perishing, probably from pneumonia when the lashing rain penetrated to the skin through their normally resilient coats. Their sufferings opened much concerned debate in deer circles about the role of badly designed, deer-forgetful fencing around blocks of forestry. This was the first time the bulk of observers were obliged to recognize the effects on deer of removing their traditional wintering grounds. Many deer died descending from higher ground and trying to find passages through the netting barriers to the shelter that low ground had always afforded them. The weather itself was not especially severe, but they could not get out of it. One thing that was noted was that deaths had occurred in places where there was no perceptible population problem. It is now accepted that the relationship between population and winter death is not simple. The grounds for reducing deer numbers for humane reasons, to prevent them dying in bad winters, have weakened.

There are arguments for reducing red deer numbers from the 300,000 level, cogent ones. It must be remembered that this figure is on a smaller range than they have ever occupied – or a smaller official range. That is why they have started to move onto unofficial range. Red deer are spreading their range and spreading it fast. Not in all areas, but particularly in areas where numbers have been multiplying. This situation affects not only Scotland but all European countries which have deer, and also the USA. The high pressure-point for Scottish deer numbers in winter 1992–3 was the east Angus glens, although the big increases in numbers had occurred all over the southern marches of the red deer range including islands such as Mull, Jura and Islay. As already mentioned, in Angus and the east Grampians deer had colonized moorland traditionally used for grouse shooting. The utilization by deer of these mineral-rich heathery glens, some of which produced the best grouse shooting in the Highlands, had happened surreptitiously. It may be hard for the layman to understand how deer can use an area without drawing attention to the fact. The answer is that deer are secretive animals, not prone to advertise their presence. Consider all the hill-walkers who stride the high tops never setting eyes on an animal which they read in the papers has enjoyed a population explosion. People who live in the Highlands will understand it better. How many farmers curse the predations of stags breaking into spring pasture at night, gone by daylight? They will knock down drystone walls with their feet to do it – even when there is netting on the outside of the wall to keep them further off. Deer in east Angus were creeping down the hillside at night and marauding onto re-seeded parklands designed for sheep. They lay off on higher ground by day. Gradually, instead of returning to the high ground, they stayed on the moor, basking in the flourishing heather. At the point at which hinds started to calve there the problem to be addressed had already become considerable. The situation was recognized first around fifteen years ago, when heather became over-grazed. The difficulties of sorting it out were exacerbated because the key estates at that time, like many others in the Highlands, tended to be secretive about their affairs; co-operation with deer culls was the exception not the rule. An attempt to organize a deer management group in 1972 was torpedoed because some important figures would not get involved.

Meanwhile the evidence of overstocking was becoming apparent on much of deer range. If the deer population had been magically uplifted into the sky tracking on hillsides and over-grazed heather would have given the game away. Dick Balharry is right in saying that the health history of the landscape is written on the ground. Tracking is a conspicuous scarring of the ground generally marking a diagonal line across hill-faces. It is caused by many hooves cutting through the herbage to the ground below, the marks becoming wider as numbers increase. Deer, like sheep, tend to move around the countryside on historically-proven routes; hill-walkers often find the deer-trots constitute the best way across a gully or awkward defile. Deer are larger than sheep and therefore the tracks that suit each are not the same. Extreme tracking on steep faces can lead to erosion and ground falling away. Over-grazing can also lead to erosion, if the plant cover is reduced to bare ground, although normally the herbage pattern changes and coarser grasses form a healing carapace. Ecologists have shown that large numbers of deer on the tops of mountains can have damaging effects on fragile high montane vegetation, effects which are exacerbated by galloping hooves. To anyone who has looked for long at Highland landscape, an over-pressurized hill betrays itself at a glance. There is no need for it, it does nothing for the production of more shootable stags, it disadvantages other moorland wildlife, it is unsightly, and the ground takes a while to recover. All of these things are true for a less-often mentioned phenomenon – under-grazing, now occuring on deer range that for a variety of reasons has been vacated by deer. But for the moment most of the problem is over-grazing and over-stocking.

Credit is due to the RDC, and to some conservation organizations, in forcing forward the agenda of professional deer management which will address this. In the face of mounting pressure, both quietly from the RDC, and publicly from conservation groups, deer forest owners and their managers have had to sharpen up their act. It was always in their interests to do so; loss of heather in east Angus benefited nobody. Deer forest owners, concerned to protect their capital values by upholding the number of stags shot, began to understand they could take the same number of stags from fewer hinds; after all, frequently hind numbers had risen without any corresponding rise in the stag cull. Furthermore larger numbers of hinds were reducing the size and quality of the stags. The proliferation of herds of hinds, monopolizing the best hefts, pushing stags onto lower ground, and performing below their best breeding potential, suited no one.

Deer forest owners in east Angus decided to take action and in the winter of 1992–3 have done so in a major way. They beefed up the numbers of people to do the job, hired drivers for the all-terrain vehicles, and were assisted for a short time by RDC stalkers, the first occasion the RDC had moved onto private ground as a roving culling force in this way. Deer numbers were reduced by 35 per cent. This simple figure will only give some idea of the sheer human effort, the elongated man-hours in sometimes atrocious conditions, the sweat and toil and tribulation that this exercise has demanded of its executioners, to those who have been actively engaged in deer culling. Something that is seldom taken into account is the emotional stress to stalkers having to shoot animals in these numbers, piled onto the physical stress. Only those who have done it, who have followed up an unmothered calf, hanging round its suddenly-deceased parent, yet somehow awkward to get a sure shot at, will understand the stress I am talking about. Stalkers are doing a job, but that does not mean they are devoid of emotions from shooting deer over a long time. No one normal enjoys shooting dependent calves; or a slaughter of hinds. A large estate cull in east Sutherland had to be interrupted for a week while stalkers recharged their psychological batteries before continuing. The naturalist David Bellamy, who understands these dilemmas, says, when addressing audiences of ultra-greens noisily opposed to field sports, he asks them point-blank whether they would be prepared to take up the rifle and do the management culls they are urging others to perform? Silence is soon restored.

The east Angus glens, and the east Grampians generally, are not the only places deer matters have been taken firmly in hand. The deer population problem has been caused by under-culling of hinds rather than stags, and the 1992–3 winter hind cull was the heaviest ever undertaken over the deer forest range, following the previous year's which was a record too. The 1991–2 hind cull was 25,000; the 1992–3 cull, not officially recorded at the time of writing, will be well over 30,000, with some 10,000 calves. A massive effort has been mounted by estates, despite the fact that there is no incentive to cull from venison prices. For most estates the hind culling operation will not have been economic. But it has been done. The percentage increase in the cull will have been nearly 30. The RDC is keen to see deer numbers down to between 250,000 and 200,000, a figure with which deer forest owners are content. At least estate deer culls have started to reduce total deer numbers, having for some years grappled with the problem of controlling incremental growth, or the expansion of natural increase. There is still more heavy culling to do. However, the chairman of the RDC, Patrick Gordon-Duff-Pennington, believes that within three years, if the matter continues to be addressed with resolution, deer numbers will be back in balance with their habitat.

From the beginning (the first counts were started in the 1950s and suggested a population of 155,000) the population increase has been localized. The west Highlands, although there have been instances of population growth, have generally been stable, and in places deer numbers have been falling. Popular mountain-walking areas such as Glencoe and around Loch Shiel have lost their deer populations almost entirely, owing to human pressures. There are forty-five deer management groups covering all deer forest range in the Highlands, each with its own story. RDC deer counts, which must be assumed the most accurate, have been problematical in recent years because ideal counting conditions, characterized by lengthy periods of snow cover when deer show up well against the whiteness, have been rare. In the last published census work, performed in 1991 on seven areas in the west Highlands, the most significant being at Gairloch, Ardnamurchan, Rhum and Ardochy/Port

Clair/Glen Moriston/Glen Urquhart treated as one block, total numbers were lower than the previous formal count several years earlier. Deer management groups can make a fair fist of carrying out a census of the deer in their areas, but where deer have strayed outside traditional deer range, for example all along the southern edge of the Highlands, and in the Borders as far south as Gatehouse, and onto the Galloway coast, certainty about numbers is less. The coming together of deer management groups, and the recently-formed Association of Deer Management Groups, collating information from all its constituent sources, will improve deer forest counting henceforth.

Counts however are just that, numerical assessments. Neither the RDC nor any deer management groups have attempted to correlate deer numbers to available habitat, sheep numbers, habitat health, forage availability, deer health and condition, age classes, and so on. Counts taken in isolation could never be used as the basis for prescribed culls over deer range in the name of ecologically exact science. A heathery hillside in the east Grampians can support far higher stocking rates than a predominantly rock escarpment in Wester Ross; high ground only suitable for grazing in summer cannot be compared to low ground supporting grass and sheltered by forestry. What determines any area's suitability for deer is the quality of the wintering ground. Sustainable densities can only be computed when other land-use interests are written in. There are arcane factors known only to stalkers over the generations which make one bit of hill better than the next for supporting deer. Every deer-stalking man knows the heaviest hinds on any forest tend to derive from a specific area, an area which may resemble those beside it, but which for some underlying mineral reason puts condition on the deer. When the RDC produced a recommended figure for culling deer stocks of one-sixth of the population annually, they acknowledged that it could not be used simplistically across the board, and that sustainability varied from place to place.

The variables in climate, seasonal growth, and all the special circumstances which separate one deer forest from another (the old firm of taxidermists in Inverness could distinguish which forest a stag emanated from by its antlers), suggest that the best way to determine culling levels for the following season is through the management group system. The stalker on the ground, or the resident deer manager or laird, is going to know best how to interpret the bare figures of censuses. Larder weights will have given him a strong indication of the bodily conditions of his deer. Examination of the hinds during the hind cull will have told what approximate proportion are carrying a calf for birth in June, and he will also have observed what proportion have a calf at foot. Most importantly there are historic records. Deer cull targets must be considered, not by predicting the following year's calving, but from what happened last year. When all is said and done, and the last bullet of the season fired, it is easy to redress over-culling – the stalker can take a holiday.

The complexity of the whole business of culling targets was powerfully demonstrated over the winter of 1992–3. As mentioned, the hind-culling season saw the most intensive deer cull ever formally undertaken in Scotland. Stalkers by 15 February when the season at last closed, were as thin as whippets. Many had been worked to their physical limits. The deer, too, were at their physical limits. The 1992–3 winter cull disclosed some thought-provoking facts. Hinds were in very poor condition. Weights at the important central Highlands forest of Ardverickie were as low as they had been since 1916. Game-dealers confirmed this picture as universal. The Grantown dealer Highland Venison reported February carcaasses 31 per cent lighter than average. Deer in many places were skin and bone.

Stalkers tactfully pushed the feebler specimens down holes in the ground rather than bring them in to shame the deer larder. Of those that went to market the government vets condemned as unfit for human consumption more beasts than usual. The key body-health indicator is the amount of fat found around the kidneys; kidney fat was low in November before the winter even got a grip. The RDC with its usual efficiency, a finger firmly on the pulse of life in the hills and glens, foresaw the situation a long way in advance. The commission had taken the unusual step of issuing to forest owners forms to be filled by the following June enumerating all carcasses found dead on the hill. In one glen in Inverness-shire 350 calves were found dead before Christmas, a bonanza for eagles, crows and foxes. In less dramatic fashion stalkers were talking sombrely about winter deaths prior to the critical time for survival, April and May. Winter deaths, for 1992–3, when the records are collated, are certain to be high. Many deaths are never put on record; corpses, especially of calves, melting away rapidly.

What are the causes? Certainly January 1993 was a hard month. There were three weeks of blizzards, snow lying on much middle to high ground, and consistent low temperatures. But three weeks is not long; an old-fashioned Highland winter lasted three months. Deer were certainly under pressure, and the cold snap will have taken more out of them. The real reasons for poor health in winter 1992–3 go further back. It all started in May 1992. Much of the Highlands had little or no rain for three months. Summer grass, off which deer fatten themselves during the short body-building period, never materialized. When it did it was poor-quality grass, too late, and too floppy. A late flush of grass is never what summer grass is. A lot of calves quietly breathed away their last over summer, their mothers lacking milk to sustain them. This impoverished summer was followed, instantly, by prolonged rain. In the late summer months the deer pack on fat for winter; this spell was cruelly inhospitable. They never had 'a dry back', as sheep stockmen put it, from end July to January. In the west Highlands August was the wettest month ever recorded. This is the key fact.

Those who hasten to attribute deer deaths in 1992–3 to over-population should think again: deer deaths were as numerous in lowly-populated areas as in densely-populated ones. The explanation lies in the weather cycle. Nor is it simply to do with the fact of rain. It is when the rain falls, or fails to fall, that matters. The December/January Highland rains, which can be heavy, do not affect deer unduly. But if they enter the winter in poor condition it is a long time to wait until first grass in April or May from which to build up recovery.

Two facts were being reported by stalkers and deer managers during the hind cull in 1992–3. There was a low proportion of hinds with calves at foot, in some places as low as one calf to six hinds (the figure would normally be around one to two), and there were very low pregnancy rates in the hinds shot. At Borrobol we found that the older hinds were bearing calves, but a substantial number of middle-aged and young hinds with no calves following, also had no calf inside them. I heard this corroborated by many stalkers, and the RDC confirmed it. Low pregnancy rates, low calf numbers, in combination with a record cull figure means the deer population problem is going into reverse. Early indicators suggest the number of calves born in 1993 may be half normal levels in some places. One additional factor which has helped redress the balance, though not in a way deer managers will relish: far more deer have been killed out of season, by farmers and crofters, than usual. Farmers and crofters reach for the rifle rather than the telephone when deer maraud, and those landowners who have tried to circumvent stags being unselectively shot out of season by offering financial compensation to crop-growers in return for the right to shoot the deer themselves, have found the wallet sorely stressed. The RDC inspects game-dealer record-books, and they show large increases in sales from the agricultural sector. Ninety per cent of out-of-season deer that reach the market are sold to game-dealers, in Louis Stewart's estimation. The proportion shot regardless of season, regardless of whose ground they are on, regard-less of the law, are another matter, one which cannot be factored into deer management group plans, nor anyone else's. As Louis Stewart wryly admitted there are some cowboys out there, banging away indiscriminately, but there are some pretty professional shooters too. They have all played their part, within and without the law, in starting to bring Scotland's deer back into balance with their habitat.

The means to do this effectively have never been ampler than now. Since the 1970s much work has been done on management of the uplands, most notably by the Macaulay Land Use Research Unit and the Institute of Terrestrial Ecology, both in Aberdeenshire. For many years scientists have been looking at the impact of sheep and deer on habitats, and also of cattle. The differences in impact of the first two are notoriously hard to separate; scientists have even had recourse to describing deer as 'brown sheep'. In broad terms the accepted generalization is that deer and sheep together form a combination of grazers that is more punishing on herbage than each acting separately. The commonest situation on Scottish hills, except in the Lowlands, is both animals grazing together. Rule-of-thumb measurements are that deer have twice the impact of sheep as individuals, but sheep outnumber deer by six to one on deer range, so collectively sheep have a bigger impact. Deer have higher energy requirements than sheep and are intrinsically less capable of survival on the hills, producing a further rule-of-thumb measurement that deer collectively have around half the impact of sheep. Their mouths differ, and mouth shape and size determine effects on the ground, combined with herbage preferences. Sheep's smaller mouths graze closer to the ground; but their herbage selection is broadly similar. Deer graze in larger groups than sheep, and tend therefore to bypass the niche-grazing pockets which individual sheep pick out. Sheep and deer have the ability, as all grazers do, to change the habitat they utilise. Heather can be grazed so low that strong grasses, usually bents and fescues, take over. Aerial photographs taken by the Scottish Office over time have enabled scientists to extrapolate from a coverage of ten per cent of Scotland, a heather-loss figure for the whole country of 25 per cent between 1945 and 1977. This alarming land-use change is considered to be half owing to afforestation with commercial softwoods, the remaining half being due to agricultural changes such as hill re-seeding programmes, along with heather loss from over-grazing. It has been noted that where there are more grazing animals the loss of heather is more pronounced.

What is also true, but less often mentioned, is that heather has powerful capacities of recolonization. Where grazing animals are excluded heather can make a fast and luxuriant reappearance. In the Pennines this can come about in one year, in Scotland it takes considerably longer. But anyone who has fenced off hill-land for forestry has witnessed first the regrowth of heather. Along Strathspey clear-felled hills have reverted to heather. Recent sheep clearances over large areas in the Highlands have also shown that where sheep are removed from the deer/sheep duo heather has the ability slowly to recolonize ground turned green by sheep. This can take place with the continuing presence of deer. Examples of this, and birch regeneration, are widespread; one is Glen Affric. As ever in a balance of land-use and habitat protection, it is a question of numbers.

When looking at habitat loss in the Highlands heather is the salient subject. Scotland has heather moorland on a scale no other country enjoys. To lose it, as has happened extensively in the Pennines, would be extremely unfortunate. The landscape lesson is there to be learned in the west Highlands. Intensive sheep grazing in alliance with uncontrolled heather-burning has removed heather cover from most of it. Scientists were not needed to make this discovery: it was apparent to anyone looking at the exclosure by fencing of the west Highland rail-line. Inside it juniper, gorse, whinbushes and heather line the track, with trees where there is space for them to grow; outside it coarse grasses stretches from mountain-top to strath-bottom.

It is reckoned that heather can withstand 40 per cent of the new shoots being grazed off. Above that figure the plant regresses and becomes stunted. If over 60 per cent of the plant's new shoots are bitten off the plant degenerates and may die. The abundance of these new shoots available for grazing varies from season to season, depending on heat and sunshine, and on rainfall. The heather-plant, technically a dwarf shrub, is astonishingly tough. Its seeds are known to lie for a minimum of 50 years without their ability to germinate being damaged. But it is vulnerable to being taken over by grasses, which are capable of smothering the slower performance of heather in its young phases. Scottish Natural Heritage has made the preservation of heather an objective, and it is laudable one. But the methods of best achieving it remain to be worked out. There is an aversion to burning heather because of the evidence of the extinction this can result in to the west. At the same time if deer and sheep are present in large numbers too, small areas of burnt ground will over-pressurize the young shoots when they are struggling to get through. Larger muir-burns may be preferable. Deer can then help crop the first emergent grasses, which start to grow almost immediately. Rank long heather supports little or no life, as is evident if it is eventually burnt off. Droppings of grouse, sheep and deer are often totally absent. In these situations sometimes re-burning is necessary to get rid of dead ground-cover. Cropping of heather, in moderation, strengthens the roots and does it good.

The last grazer in the moorland equation, relevant especially to lower ground, is the cow. To the detriment of moorlands cattle have largely departed the scene. This has significance for deer. When the late Lord Dulverton owned the deer forest of Glenfeshie, cattle were employed at the end of summer to graze the fertilized grasses which were to winter the deer. In a number of places where grazing regimes without cattle have got out of hand the big, wide, bovine mouths have had to be recalled, valued for their ability to mow unselectively, cropping rough grasses with rich ones, and promoting soil fertility and nutrient cycles through their dunging. There is now a cry for more cattle in the hills, for their benefits as tools of herbage management. The difficulties of this are economic and practical. Cattle do not lie out in winter untended, as sheep and deer have the potential to do. Winter feeding is needed, it is bulky, and it is expensive.

Dunging and urine effects are themselves a complex subject. They depend on underlying vegetation and general land-feature factors. The same high-up, or montane, woolly fringe moss that is damaged by trampling from excessive deer numbers, and that is sensitive to acid rain, is harmed by urine and dung. The woolly fringe moss, which delicately carpets Scotland's high tops, gets its sustenance from rainfall not from the soil. Urine prevents the plant from metabolizing efficiently and promotes the growth of grasses which can then smother the moss. Mosses are hard to re-establish, and Britain is particularly rich in moss and lichen varieties. By contrast grasses are annuals, they are common, and they colonize quickly. The arguments for looking after our precious and rare Highland habitat are powerful, and the scentists who draw our attention to them must be listened to. High-ground plant communities are an example of a commodity deserving protection. The people who have done the research, and worked hard and long to try and assess different ecological impacts, are sharply to be distinguished from those who would manipulate their findings selectively to make widespread prescriptions against deer populations *per se*. Dr Des Thompson, chief scientist at Scottish Natural Heritage, having once been the author of broad-brush deer culling targets, now believes we should adhere to culling targets on an area basis, taking account of all the elements which can be factored into a sophisticated equation. He believes there should be some form of framework for monitoring the health of all plant communities comprising the habitat, and that deer man-agement groups, along with the RDC and Scottish Natural Heritage, should use these disciplines to help determine the deer populations which can live in balance with the land.

With the future of sheep farming in the hills at risk from the progressive withdrawal of its subsidy lifeline, the entire land use picture may be due to change in the most radical way since large-scale sheep farming arrived in the Highlands 200 years ago. In many parts of the world, including parts of Europe, the cessation of marginal agriculture is creating second generation scrub and wilderness. In America this is happening on the plains of the Midwest where ghost towns testify to the cattle ranchers who used to eke out a state-supported subsis-tence. In Scotland deer would be the major beneficiaries of a reverse Clearances, and hinds would range further up the hill. Patterns of deer movement, and mixes of the underlying vegetation, not to mention social mixes, would change. In England some wildlife areas have got out of hand and grazing animals – goats, ponies, sheep – have had to be recalled to trim them down again. It is not beyond believing that in fifty years we will be calling for the return of sheep, for herbage management purposes, as we are doing now for cows.

# Chapter 6

It is one of the more annoying contemporary tendencies that the media represent fringe opinion as mainstream. The more amazing your viewpoint the more likely it is to get an airing. This has happened spectacularly with the red deer issue. For two years at least no newspaper editor, or programme maker, has been able to feel he has covered the waterfront until he has done a big piece on red deer. Such is the dispiriting conformity of media opinion that virtually all comment on the red deer has flowed from the same direction – the province of ultra-greenery. Frequently the holders of this viewpoint start their lamentations with a complaint that they are never listened to! On one radio programme the interviewer asked an ecologist why, given the obvious sense of his prescription for the obliteration of red deer on the old Caledonian Forest local people questioned by radio inter-viewers had a different view? He said this was because they had been brainwashed! By whom, and how, was not volunteered.

Thus it is that the body which has been dealing with Scotland's red deer since its inception in 1959, the Red Deer Commission (RDC), is seldom given more than a token hearing when deer are up for discussion. This is a pity because the RDC has done a difficult job well. Its rangers know more about the deer, have seen more of them in widely differing situations, and brokered more negotiations with difficult deer forest owners or stalkers, than will ever be told. Their remit refers to the impact of deer on forestry and agriculture and they have become artful in the use of persuasion in achieving their ends. Sensitized over time to the politico/socio overtones of deer forests the RDC has seen coming from a long way off the dangers of the campaign to have them vested with more powers. A beefed-up RDC is one of the aims held in common by most groups purporting to have an interest in land use and land-use change. The two primary muscles conservationists would like to see the RDC equipped with are: powers to make landowners cull, and a change in the RDC remit to make it responsible for protection of the 'natural heritage' as well as agriculture and forestry. Upon the meaning of the phrase 'natural heritage' hangs a great deal. It is already clear that protection of the heather is supposed to come under this heading, and indeed heather measurement techniques have been designed so that the health of the plant can be decided. Commissioners have spotted that if their powers are increased in this way they will be expected to use them. Touring the country measuring the heather might become a routine duty, not one which old-timers on the deer scene can envisage with relish. There was an attempt during the parliamentary passage of the Scottish Natural Heritage Bill to get the Deer (Scotland) Act amended in this way, but the government rejected it.

The RDC has also been rebuked by greens for not being as fractious and radical as some other government agencies acting in the field of environment. The former NCC managed to get the country fraternity united in arms against it, something no other body had ever achieved. The RDC has formed working relationships with landowners that have been typecast by outsiders as too friendly. The failure to act early on the hind population explosion was presented as an example of the problems of this cosy relationship. In fact, the commission had been exhorting heavier culls for some time, exhortations which were eventually heeded; but the slowness of landowner response in some areas was more to do with the novelty of the predicament, and practical difficulties of putting high culls suddenly into operation, than structural problems with deer management. Activists whose hidden agenda is to take over the RDC by changing its membership are unlikely to admit this. Calls for a more modern RDC, championing such concepts as conservation of the 'natural heritage', and heather (referred to quasi-scientifically as 'semi-natural range'), have been heard. Another line of attack has been to propose that the RDC loses its independence and becomes subsumed in a broader rural organization to whom it would be accountable.

It is onto this scene that a very unusual figure in Highland affairs came to rest or rather to rampage, as the RDC chairman, appointed in 1992. Patrick Gordon-Duff-Pennington had already, as the convener of the Scottish Landowner's Federation, etched himself on the minds of many people. His public method is to charm and amuse rather than cajole. His typical mode in public-speaking is to tear his jacket from his back when he reaches the podium, and roll up his sleeves. He then mixes stories and reminiscences with shrewdly-inserted thoughts, not all of them comfortable for all of the audience. In fact, he pulls no punches. He talks tough, but with a tongue of silver. He is a countryman with a passionate concern for the hills and a deep knowledge of sheep and deer and ecological balance; above all he sees people as part of the natural equation in the Highland context; to lose them would, in his book, be to lose the battle. Accordingly he favours no course of action prejudicial to local employment. On deer forests that means stalkers. He once defined the purpose of owning land as 'to employ people'.

A theme that recurs in his addresses is kinship with the land. He is dismayed by ownership of land which is not in sympathy with the soil and what the ground can sustain. He believes the connection with land must be strengthened. He sees that extreme green views need to be strident to get media attention, and money; and wishes for an alliance of interests by all those who sincerely have the well-being of the Highlands at heart, and are not motivated by other agendas. On the subject of absentee ownership, one of the more ticklish problems for estate management in the Highlands, he feels a degree vexed. Whilst acknowledging that estate ownership is either a costly indulgence, or very gritty financial going (he is one of the owners of the deer forest of Ardverickie), and recognizing that money earned in the south is the life-blood of much employment and much of the way of life in the north, he is unhappy about the type of absenteeism which becomes so pronounced that stewardship of the land falters, and a mess develops. More Scottish landowners in possession of grouse-moors live on their ground than deer forest owners. Particularly in the north and north-western deer range the landowners often live far off, and connections with what is going on become tenuous. He regrets the necessity for this, and notes wryly that the further south the landowner resides the harder it is to extract dues for the local deer management group, or the umbrella Association of Deer Management Groups. He thinks we should approach our deer management more professionally, and become more skilled and conversant with ageing deer. He works harmoniously with Scottish Natural Heritage, and is prone to respond to pushing from them by pointing out that, with a budget of some £400,000 his financial resources are 1 per cent of theirs. Above all with his ability to talk profitably to anyone he has de-demonized landowners to the greens, and successfully defused some of the antagonisms which were threatening to end in sterile confrontation.

However, the problem between landowners and their critics has never been one entirely of perception. The fact of land-ownership is itself offensive to many, not least to those who use the deer debate to advance ends which are fundamentally political. There are two strands in anti-landlordism in Scotland, and they need to be distinguished. One hails from native Highlanders who have adopted the scepticism of their forebears based on historical experience. Distaste for the owners of land dates from as far back as the twelfth century, when following the Norman Conquest Highland hunting reserves were presented to faithful nobles in recognition of their military services. Like the Vikings before them the new land-holders or land-grabbers came from far away, and were remote from Gaeldom. Like the Vikings they tended to blend and meld, often through intermarriage, with the natives. In more recent times the nineteenth-century English who bought Highland property on the heels of Queen Victoria blended less well. They seldom took up residence; the Highlands were a summering retreat. These families are thinning out now, and the old truism that the owners of deer forests came from money that originated in drink fortunes or tobacco fortunes is being made obsolete by the calamities of Lloyds insurance liabilities, and long-term changes in social fortunes and perspectives. Owning a deer forest is not the smart adornment it once was; big game shooting is not altogether socially acceptable. It is seldom mentioned, but land-ownership in the deer forests is changing rapidly. A tranche of new buyers came from riches acquired during the late 1980s. A substantial number of the new lairds are themselves Scots. It was always said that the Scots never bought Highland estates because they were too canny; loss-making propositions lacked appeal. It has been proved untrue. What remains to be seen is whether the native roots of many of the new lairdhood are capable of overcoming traditional estrangements amongst the locals from 'the big hoos'. The portrayal of Highland lairds as mostly foreign has always been absurd: foreign owners are extremely few and far between. A factual analysis of land-ownership in the Highlands shows instead a surprising thing: that the old clan families have to a remarkable extent, despite the tearaway characteristics of many a son of the house, held on to their patrimonies. The largest land-holders in most of the Highland counties are still hereditary families. This fact explains the hesitation many native Highlanders palpably feel for denouncing the laird in front of the microphone or the camera. There are those, certainly, who believe the Clearances, and the anglicization of the ruling chiefdoms, should never be forgiven, but the sentiment is far from universal, and it is a mistake to represent mixed, equivocal and complex feelings as a situation of polarized attitudes.

The second strand of anti-landlordism is quite different. This hails from those motivated by social envy, or envy of money, and has no roots in the Highlands (Highlanders consider no-one their social superior, and are fonder of spotting the pitfalls of owning money than wishing it was all theirs). Typically this voice calls for democratic management of the land through local committees, the break-up of large land-holdings, and the subordination of- landowners to academically-decided recipes for land management following models generally termed conservationist. A programme which is motivated by a hidden political agenda can usually be determined by the absence, or only token presence, of the subject of sport. Sporting use in most of the prescriptions for the rejuvenated Highlands is mentioned as an unimportant ancillary to the wider aim of restoring the soil, forming a land-base for the future, and other windy propositions. The other giveaway characteristic of themes for replacing landowners is the call for unspecified quantities of public money. The private purse is to be replaced by the public one.

Other recent changes have a significance for the way landlords are seen. Apart from the trend towards company, or syndicate, ownership of the deer forests, and the continuing increase in land-holdings belonging to charities (the RSPB is one of the largest landowners in the Highlands), local people have arrived on the scene as substantial owners of land with the purchase of North Lochinver Estate by a consortium of one hundred-odd crofters. This has set a precedent for all land under crofting tenure, in other words much of the west Highlands and the outer isles. The North Lochinver case was interesting on several counts. It was hailed by the media in Scotland as a victory for people power, as the people routing the wicked landlord, and fit comeuppance for a foreigner buying land as a speculative venture. The technical position was that a determined, well-led, publicity-aware group of local crofters perceived the fundamental insecurity of a landlord whose ground was almost entirely under crofting tenure. Crofting tenure is hereditable and consists of inalienable grazing rights. The freeholds of crofts may be bought up by crofters, subject to permission being granted from the government regulator, the Crofters' Commission. By threatening to exercise their right to buy their crofts the crofters at Noth Lochinver indicated to the selling agents that the residual sporting and other rights, in this case anyway negligible, were well-nigh worthless. Any new landowner would be owner only in name, possessed of more liabilities in his role as feudal superior than useful rights. The outcome of the protracted negotiations for the sale, conducted in the full public eye, was that the crofters' consortium, with the aid of public sector loans, purchased the freehold of a large parcel of land complete with trout lochs and some marginal stalking. Already

114

another crofters bid is under way for ownership of more west coast croft-land. One of the ways out of the dilemma of how to make these land-holdings pay is an accord with rich organizations such as the RSPB, which has been trumpeting the environmental friendliness of crofting *vis-à-vis* its non-intensive land use practices. The more financially astute crofters know well that the achievement of ownership has now to be matched with the far harder one of staying in place. Those who have always belaboured the landlords now face the landlords' dilemma. Financial rigour is a marvellous equalizer. The gulf of rhetoric between crofters and lairds, as their destinies merge, may become smaller.

There are more reasons than money for landowners and crofters to find common cause. The shrinking of space in Britain is felt by everyone whose undisturbed life in the outback is now experiencing encirclement from those demanding access. The access question has become steadily more acute, and seems to be one in which moderation, and sensible concession, are hard to find. It is particularly pertinent to deer management.

The conflict of interest is not only between hill-walkers and stalking parties. From the deer point of view a critical time when the animals require peace and quiet is calving, in late May and early June. This is because of the way hinds give birth, and the nature of the risks from predators. Hinds feeling their time is ripe move away from the main group and lie down in a sheltered place. When the calf is born they leave it, hidden in the vegetation, for several days, returning only to suckle it. The mother might stray a mile away. During this time disturbance from passers-by puts the calf at risk. People coming on calves, snuggled down in the grass, are tempted to pick them up and start looking for the mother. This takes the calf from its known resting-place, and smears alien scents on it which can lead to mis-mothering. In some parts of the

Highlands as many as 5 per cent of deer calves are eaten by eagles, and foxes account for many more. The dislocation of calf and mother from human disturbance exaggerates this already heavy predation rate. When hind numbers are too high it is harder to plead that deer need to be left in peace at calving. Numbers, however, should not alter basic conscientiousness about wildlife safekeeping. It may also be legitimately argued that eagles and foxes too deserve their sustenance; if not they eat more lambs etc, etc. But the problem highlights a point which is always mentioned by country people when considering how to facilitate access for the masses. The wildlife which is part of the draw to the hills is often not noticed and seldom understood by those who track over its territory. Shepherds and stalkers, eyes trained to their ground and spying detail at distance, and interpreting it, are constantly fed with a stream of information while traversing the hills most of which is completely elusive to someone versed in a landscape of concrete. This is no-one's fault, and it cannot easily be rectified, but it is perhaps useful background understanding to why the access debate finds people confronting each other at the outset with something less than respect.

There is another thing. Most hill-walkers respect the property and ground on which they relax and stretch their limbs. They understand that their playground is another man's workplace. It has become more usual for walkers to ask the stalker, during the stalking season, which routes they can take without inconveniencing him. But hill-walking is a natural activity not given to containment or formalization within a club or fraternity. Most walkers belong to no association or group. However, the groups that represent them advance a considerably more militant profile than the huge bulk of walkers would wish. The point of view of the Ramblers' Association seems to be: the countryside is ours to do as we please

in; all encumbrances enfringe our rights. This is uncon-
structive and confrontational, as well as being unrepre-
sentative. The same attitude in reverse can occasionally
be found in stalkers and their employers. A stalker tends
naturally to regard the wide horizon as his domain. He is
out there, after all, in the worst weather, and knows the
territory's every crevice. Landowners can fall into a pro-
prietorial attitude to land which is logically absurd: the
cliché that no one owns land, but they only look after it
for a while, is completely true. Contemporary culture has
changed the nature of ownership. I recall the remark of
a man who had just bought a Highland estate in a remote
place. He said, 'Now I can get away from it all'. I sympa-
thized with his feeling – he was an extremely hard-
working man whose efforts contribute much to our
national economy – but I cannot sympathize with his
reasoning and interpretation of ownership. Our islands
are too small for parcels of land to be carved out and
protected for the purposes of solitude. Deer forest
owners of ground which is popular with walkers and
climbers are caught in an unenviable cleft-stick: on the
one hand the necessity to control their deer population
by culling twinned with the need to reap commercial
rents from stalking lets, on the other the difficulties,
sometimes impossibilities, of doing so because of disturbance. In the most walked-over parts of the Highlands
deer have either departed the scene, or have acclimatized
themselves to human passers-by. This acclimatization can
be their undoing when the passer-by carries a rifle up his
sleeve and needs to fill his freezer. If walkers keep to
specific routes it is remarkable to what extent deer will
tolerate them; departure from familiar routes causes
sudden consternation and sometimes, in montane
habitats, environmental damage as deer run helter-
skelter. One of the most awkward things is that deer run
from scents sooner than sights. Few users of the hills are

wondering where their scents are travelling. In the southern Highlands forest owners have sometimes decided to leave parts of the ground for walkers and not attempt to stalk there. This is all right if the ground is big enough. For smaller forests it is impracticable. Then, much depends on the stalker. I was told by a stalker on a national nature reserve that he was only forced to abandon the day once in eleven years on account of walkers. But he had no paying rifles to cater for. The stalker with a man breathing down his neck who has paid his whack for the day, and watches his chosen stag get up and unaccountably depart, is a man under pressure. There is the added pressure of having to consider, in the use of a high-velocity rifle, the trajectories of any conceivable ricochet or miss and the complete safety of every shot.

Two things are happening and will continue to happen. Those deer forests with the ground prized by walkers which reaches 3000 feet will experience increased visitor numbers. An agent recently told me the first requirement now for prospective deer forest owners was the absence of significant 'Munros' or 3000-foot mountains. The second is a concomitant of the first: deer will disappear from the popular high tops, and also from the foothills where they winter. Hinds will not successfully rear calves there, and therefore the hefted deer population will drift away. Damage from the hooves of our big mammals will be replaced by damage from the hiking-boot. Deer range, in this regard, will shrink. It seems inconceivable that land will ever be set aside by law for sporting purposes and in future stalking will have to squeeze into the gap left by other land-users. Education about deer, a subject with which most people are keen to acquaint themselves, will increase and will, hopefully, lessen the impacts of land-uses which are partially incompatible. On one estate I know the presence of a youth hostel in the middle is actually regarded by the stalker as an advantage: a superintendent is resident from June to October and he informs and advises hikers about the deer and keeps them off the critical ridges when stalking is in progress. The stalker, in turn, with the use of a hill-vehicle, makes life easier for the remotely-located superintendent. Almost certainly publicity about the problems of the deer cull have made the country-going public more understanding when stalkers plead leave to pursue their tasks unhindered. Ronnie Rose, at his Wildlife Centre at Eskdalemuir, says that 95 per cent of visitors are prepared to listen to a reasoned argument with regard to stalking and deer control. The Edwardian stalking experience, however, when the stalking party had unchallenged freedom of the hills and shared it with their quarry, has already gone. If the mountain-ridge in the morning shows a bare back to the sky, most stalkers, in the recesses of their minds, are waiting for that bobbing line of bright anoraks to put in its appearance, somewhere, sometime.

# Chapter 7

When William Scrope in 1839 wrote about the principal deer forests in Scotland he enumerated thirty-nine. This was before the great vogue for deer stalking at the turn of the century. In his classic *The Deerstalking Grounds of Great Britain and Ireland* written in 1960, Kenneth Whitehead named around 550 deer forests in Scotland. Thirty years later, as a result of subdivision and the spread of the deer range, the RDC is taking annual deer cull returns from 650 estates, some of which are large farms on the west coast onto which deer periodically stray, and some of which are only periodically contributing to the cull. Almost all of the deer forest cull derives from a maximum of 445 forests.

A major component of the deer cull is from the owners of woodland, private and public sector. The Forestry Commission is the biggest deer culler in Scotland with an annual cull of over 6000. The Commission's cull has levelled out and stayed roughly the same since the 1970s, as the deer population has stabilized and timber rotations have entered their second cycle. Private sector woodlands are typically younger, more diverse, and only now starting to maintain a stabilized population of deer. The private sector cull is also around 6000. The remaining three-quarters of the annual cull comes from the big sporting estates, the biggest of which have several stalking beats, each with its own stalker.

The critical mass arguments for deer managed on large areas of ground have already been gone into. Small slices of deer forests, the artificial fragmentation by sporting marketeers of partially self-contained areas, tends to result in unprofessional management, absentee ownership, potting at deer in an opportunistic way when they happen to be passing, and seriously stretched finances often culminating in the disappearance of the stalker. This is good news for locals who enjoy eating venison. Deer require to be managed on an extensive basis: the creation of regional deer management groups is an implicit recognition of the benefits to be gained from co-operation, and a method of management appropriate to an animal that occupies unfenced territory stretching in parts of Scotland from coast to coast. Unilateral actions by one estate in the centre of deer range makes an impact on the neighbours; stalkers have always known this and there has been abundant proof. In 1992 the Association of Deer Management Groups was formed both to co-ordinate deer policy on a national scale, and also to explore ways to develop the market for venison. Many people see the recovery of value to venison as an essential ingredient of a healthy deer scene. The creation of the Association has shown that deer managers are willing and prepared to quell public unease about high deer numbers and act in unison to take their responsibility seriously. This was underpinned by the record hind cull of winter 1992–3. It is the first time free-wheeling and *ad hoc* management of deer has been wrested from private individuals, and although the Association has no statutory power, its authors believe they will be able to wield sufficient clout, and bring adequate force to bear, to root out abuses embarrasing to the majority. This is appropriate if deer managers believe what they claim – that they are managing the most important mammal resource of all.

In making the management of deer forests more accountable it has sometimes been possible to forget what the forests are for – the sport of stalking, the most venerable form of hunting known to man. It is easy to forget too that stalking is fundamentally a form of big game hunting. As we go into the twenty-first century what shape is it in? How is this ancient pursuit faring? In this regard Scottish stalking is interesting. Despite the options to make the sport easier and less physically demanding it is still conducted in much the way it was a century and a half ago. True, we do not embark on the track of a stag with implacable intent as the famed Victorian sportsman Charles St John did, nor stay out on the hill for a week, the encounter culminating in hand-to-horn combat struggling in floodwaters. But by and large we do as our fathers did, tramping over the hill to get close to deer, then crawling in as prostrate as a fox for a shot from a hidden position. The geography dictates it as much as tradition; there is simply no other way to get near deer that is practical. In certain places vehicles are over-used, but frequently the stalking guests protest if too much of the effort is sub-tracted from the achievement. Sporting satisfaction, like many physical satisfactions, needs to stretch people's capa-bilities. We have the telescopic-sighted rifle, and the all-terrain vehicle to carry the stag home, but essentially the sportsman of the past would know what we are about today and understand it. A glance at other European sporting cultures shows that Scotland is not alone. In every country, whether driving red deer with hounds to lines of men with double-barrelled rifles in Spain (the dogs eat the wounded deer whole!), or finishing off cornered wild boar in Portugal (performed by women clad in heavy leather skirts and armed with long daggers), or deer hunting in France where the head huntsman administers the *coup de grâce* to the stag at bay with his sword, old traditions are preserved for the sake of the thing. One Czechoslovakian pheasant shoot is managed today with full ceremonial, as it has been since the regulations were laid down in 1852. There are over thirty ordained arrangements for laying out the game at day's end, each strictly adhered to and dependent on the size of the bag. In these ways sportsmen and women feel themselves part of an old tradition, the seriousness of taking life from God's creatures is stressed, and social continuity is refreshed. Fieldsports are subject to change like any other recreation, but there is evidence that in deer stalking and hunting it is backwards to old-fashioned modes that we are pointing, most abundantly clear in America where there are numerous devotees of black powder and the crossbow. Anything which cheapens the deer hunting experience must be rigorously suppressed. So, in Scotland, the stalker who knows the value of these things maintains the traditions of gentlemanly courtesy, and entertains his guest with tales of the hill, and his knowledge of the terrain and what subsists on it. What is often forgotten by the critics of stalking is that part of the pleasure for visiting sportsmen is to meet the people who embody the countryside and have listened to the muted and mysterious music of the hills, and spend time with them in their environment. The stalk itself is part of the day, not its only purpose. Whilst the Highlands have Highlanders, that will continue to be the case.

The Highland form of stalking deer is unique, the only open-hill deer hunting of its type. Part of the day's enjoyment is landscape, openness and spatial freedom. The Highland's preciousness as one of the last wild areas in Europe only grows with time. It has been mentioned previously that German hunters, who had become the bread-and-butter stalking tenantry during the 1970s and 80s, have for the time being transferred their attentions to the east. The one immutable advantage Scottish stalking has is its landscape backdrop and the open-hill experience. A French stalker I recently spoke to brushed aside my mention of reasonable heads to be seen here at Borrobol and said simply, we come to Scotland for the exercise. Stalking has never been 'fun for the family', and in the lists of today's recreations its appeal has obvious strictures. It is unsocial, uncomfortable, and risking becoming unfashionable. It has been marginalized by English stalking people as a variation on the main, internationally-accepted theme of roe deer stalking in woodlands, and as the number of roe swells in Scotland – the population has been estimated at 400,000 – there is a possibility that red deer stalking, the form most picturesquely engraved on the popular mind, will become marginalized by roe stalking in Scotland too. Interfacing between the two, some imaginative developments have been going on in the Highlands which demonstrate the inventiveness that circumstances have brought to the surface.

The mention of stalking red deer in enclosed areas elicits a knee-jerk response of beetle-browed disapproval from the traditionalists. It need not. As always in field-sports it is the manner of presentation that determines the quality of the experience. I have seen a fascinating stalking diversification in action on a small area of hill-ground outside classical deer range, which shows what a professional approach can achieve. The enclosed area is on a hillside, so landscaped that the deer-fence is never visible over much of its length; there is the impression of the open-hill theatre of action. On the hillside are several woodlands, including some impenetrable thickets. The stags have developed special techniques and responses to being hunted in this area. They adopt strategic viewing positions high up, and rake the landscape below in the surety that approaches from behind are impossible. If so much as a pipit flits they rise slowly to their feet and march in file sedately into the trees, from which they may not emerge for the remainder of daylight. The hunter, accompanied by the stalker, is allowed to shoot only one predetermined beast, so satisfaction is far from assured. Titillation, however, is guaranteed, for the stags have been selectively bred using some of the best stock available in Europe or anywhere else, nurtured to full maturity nearby on a rotation of natural, unfertilized grass leys, and they are massive. They tower over comparable trophies in other countries; so do the costs of bagging them. The difficulties of getting them are acute. The whole operation has been designed by someone who knows deer, and knows sporting satisfaction. Before anyone rushes to emulate this exemplary set-up I should mention that the operator is one of the top deer breeders and has developed his blood-lines over a lifetime. The point to be made is that here is an inspired use of unpromising hillside. Nothing comparable could generate the revenue, provide the satisfaction, and underpin such stalker employment. Already a great deal of red deer are shot in woodlands in Scotland: this operation shows to what heights the thing can be taken. If we are serious about using regenerated native woodlands for sport then operations such as this are an instructive model. What must be understood straight off is that such results require commitment, pre-planning, a comprehension of what stalking is all about, and a high degree of professionalism.

Specialized sporting developments, and niche markets in fieldsports, are things Scotland is suited to exploring. There is the space to do it, and there is a deep pool of understanding and experience about sport. Barring hostile, prohibitive legislation (and no-one is any longer capable of predicting what irrationalities will stream from Brussels), sporting enhancements have one colossal advantage. They are dependent not on state funds, only the acquiescence of the state. They are net contributors to national revenues, a single tower of financial independence in a setting clotted with subsidized dependants. The one requirement of sporting uses is that they have the acquiescence of the public at large. The furore about red deer population imbalances has disturbed opinion outside the Highland communities, and spawned the feeling that landowners have been lax and unfitted for their duties. One vital precondition to resurrecting the image of Scottish stalking is solving the numbers game and defusing the criticism of slack management and deer over-population. A fee-paying stalking client does not want to read that his quarry is so numerous it has acquired the status of vermin. The twin status of the stag season as a cull and also a sporting engagement is only sustainable once numbers are balanced and the red deer has been restored to respectability.

The reason focus has fixed on the red deer is part of its historic association with privilege and higher social ranks. The red deer has been the victim of its own magnificence. The proliferation of muntjak and roe, in different contexts just as serious for British fauna and flora, has escaped popular censure because the smaller deer are not associated, in Britain, with snobbery and the paraphernalia of prestige. Nor are they so conspicuous, or so emotion-stirring. In this sense, showing we are serious about managing the animal that has become synonymous with the romantic grandeur of Nature, and a symbol in its own right, is of paramount importance if we can claim that we are able to manage wildlife at all. Big mammals are particularly important because in so many countries they have been wiped out. In America the bison herds dropped from numbers beyond computation to a handful of survivors rescued by a handful of ranchers. Now bison are being restored to their former range and bison-meat is reappearing on down-country menus (when the meat is valued an animal's safety is assured: the cowboys left the huge bison carcasses rotting on the plains). Many big animals have been brought back from the brink. Here in Britain a deer species – Père David's deer – was nurtured in a wildlife park whilst it died out in its homelands in China, and is presently subject to a

126

reintroduction programme. As William Conway of the New York Zoological Society put it, 'From a place where people were surrounded by animals, the world has become a place where wild animals are surrounded by people'. Red deer is the critical test for our culture, our relationship with Nature, and our values *vis-à-vis* other sentient beings.

# Chapter 8

It is unlikely that our long-term experience of managing red deer is about to fail at the time when knowledge of the animal is most developed. It would be premature to comment on what is likely to happen with the forthcoming review of the Deer (Scotland) Act, scheduled loosely for 1994, but the paper put out by the Scottish Office for consultation in 1992 was commendably intelligent and balanced. The interests of forestry, agriculture and other land-uses were all taken into account, and there was no sign that the extreme conservationist ideologies had been accommodated. This must have been a relief not only for traditional land-users, but also for bodies such as Scottish Natural Heritage, who run the risk of being aligned with impractical ideologues who court unpopularity as if it were a badge of pure intent. Scotland is particularly fortunate, during the period deer legislation review was under way, in having as the Agriculture Minister a man versed in countryside matters, Sir Hector Monro. One of the quietest members of a government labouring under diverse difficulties, Sir Hector has nonetheless played an invaluable role over the years, and been a background member of most of the mainstream bodies which have been shaping policy. Scotland is lucky in having one of the few politicians in office with whom countrymen and women can identify in an age when politicians have tended to emanate from the ranks of lifetime insiders, versed principally in political arts, experts in jockeying for position within their departments and offices at the expense of knowing how their constituents tick. Not only is Sir Hector a countryman who knows what life is like at 4 a.m. in the lambing-shed, but he is of an age when political ambition has cooled. He came late in life to his post and his performance makes a mockery of those who suggest that politicians should be younger and friskier, as initially many did at his appointment. His presence is a check on deer legislation getting out of hand. In an April visit to the RDC in Inverness he committed more money to the commission's budget for the current year, and confirmed that he had somehow wrung a commitment from the Treasury for budgetary increases to continue.

To date I have commented on the anti-deer lobby getting obstreperous. This has only happened because they have found their animadversions on land-use and abuse riding unchallenged as a convenient media headline. Landowners have always been fair game in Scotland, a circumstance which has had the odd effect of rooting them more fixedly in popular culture. Not, of course, that they are popular, but popular culture demands stereotypes: the latter-day Edwardian in tatty tweeds with twirling moustaches, or the *arriviste* English financier striding the hills with a gun in one hand and a portable telephone in the other, is now a figure permanently rooted in popular demonology, without whom the shooting lodges would seem deficient. Blame for the explosion in deer numbers can handily be put at his door, or drawbridge. Most simplifications rely on a grain of truth. Whilst the caricature of the landowner is silliness, the underlying truth is that landowners should have seen the deer numbers mounting. One wonders why they did not.

Patrick Gordon-Duff-Pennington's phrase comes back to mind: 'some landowners are divorced from the land'. It is not only true of landowners, it is true of the populace in

Britain. The difference is that landowners ought not to be. The criticism may be true of a minority. But if those deer forest owners had been on their ground, looking at changes in the vegetation, if they had been out during the hind cull, looking at larder weights and calf ratios, if they had studied age classes of cull stags from the analysis of jaw-bones (now made simple with help from the RDC), they would surely have taken note and made further enquiries. Many deer forest owners do not do these things. There is nothing new in that. What is new is that in order to trim costs they no longer employ the people who used to do it – estate factors. Only the very big estates have factors living on the place, overseeing a large work-force, but until the last twenty years most estates had the use of an estate agency factor who would watch over the estate both in general terms, and in particular detail too. Such a person might have a portfolio of fifteen to twenty estates on his books. Faced by the slump in venison prices many lairds have forgone the use of a factor imagining that their own intermittent attentions, at long distance, would suffice to keep management on track. This has proved a cruel delusion. The lairds who live on their estates and partici-pate in the work are answerable only to themselves for poor policies, but the problems usually arise when landlords are absentee.

Absentee lairds have had to rely on someone for guidance and the most obvious person has been the stalker. He resides on the ground and is in daily touch with his stock of deer. In the stalkers' defence this is sometimes a disadvantage: too close a view hides the broader picture. But stalkers in some instances have been guilty of giving misleading advice. Stalkers cannot be, and never should have been used as, cut-price factors. Their role is looking after the deer. They are not all-round estate managers and they may lack the wider perspec-tives. Stalkers also have a motive for keeping deer numbers high. The keenest dread at the back of a stalker's mind is advancing onto the hill with a paying client at heel to find no deer to stalk. Older stalkers with creaking limbs may be none too disappointed if what deer are around are close at hand. A heavy deer stock suits stalkers who look to their own convenience first. It used to be said, as a tribute to the Clearances (which were conducted by factors who then themselves became the tenant farmers), that the Highlands had been ruined by the factors. Now it is their absence that is felt. The under-shooting of hinds and the resulting lopsided deer population were on occasion caused by stalkers' indolence too. As the value of traditional perks, such as deer tusks, sinews, etc. waned, financial incentives to cull hard and face the tough winter weather declined. However, blame for the crisis in deer numbers should go to the top. Ultimately, whatever the reasons in different circumstances, landowners are responsible for misman-agement. If they were not looking hard enough, they should have been. Their role in today's society is being carefully watched. Ownership of large areas of beautiful country will be tolerated whilst it benefits the state and keeps the ground in good heart. If it becomes slipshod a cry will arise, and there will be no shortage of soothsay-ers who will climb onto the bandwagon, for the removal of those responsible. Land-ownership, and the destiny of the laird, is in the hands of the incumbents. It behoves them to do their job with care and responsibility. With the deer crisis Highland estates ceased to be pleasure play-grounds if they ever were. The mismanagement of deer brought landowners into the public eye, a slot from which they have always, often for good motives, shrunk. Stating their case and justifying their performance is no longer an option; it is vital for their continuance and for the continuance of sporting use. The truth of this is felt acutely by many in Scotland and there is profound unease about exceptional cases of incompetence imperilling the rest.

Stalkers always knew what is now empirically proved, that too many hinds lowered the quality of the stags. But to improve that they could resort to winter-feeding, beefing up the stags with concentrates; hay, potatoes, molasses, or whatever. Winter feeding of deer is a fraught subject. It started thousands of years ago, not twenty years ago as routinely written, when early man wanted his food and clothing and implement-making resource to be handy, not lost in the forests. We feed the birds in winter without thinking about it, in all probability a munificence which disadvantages them with diseases caught from crowding more than it helps them endure winters which have become progressively milder. But it is fun to watch them flocking to the hand-outs. So it is with deer. The key feeding period is January until springtime, a period when stalkers often have little other work to do. It keeps them in touch with their deer, principally the stags for hinds are more hefted and harder to persuade to feed, and it prevents winter stags wandering onto lower ground into the arms of protein-hungry farmers and crofters. It can be presented to the boss as a way of protecting his deer herd and of improving his stags. An unanticipated corollary is that it has also helped bring about the burgeoning deer populations. The extent to which this is true is unknown, and probably less than would initially be supposed. But winter feeding must have had some effect in dragging through the winter beasts which might otherwise have died off.

The politics of deer feeding are complicated. It has now become an established thing over much of deer range. Stalkers like it. On the other hand people see springtime deer walking the roadside indifferent to human traffic and find it hard to imagine that shooting these amiable and unafraid animals for sport is really sporting. The fact that the same stag which sticks its head into the Land-Rover trailer in mean weather in January is as wary as a wildcat by September is not always understood by laymen. Feeding deer in winter brings these wild animals one small step closer to becoming a form of semi-domesticated stock and in a so-far marginal way, to the untutored mind, it compromises the image of stalking wild animals as a sport. This is not the head on which conservationists disapprove of winter feeding. Their point is that it is artificial, and has inadvertently damaged habitat by helping deer numbers grow and also by concentrating the deer presence in winter when the ground is singularly unable to tolerate it. Deer feeding areas do look messy and trampled-up in springtime, but I have noticed that what often recolonizes these feed-areas when feeding is moved is original heather, not grasses. Failure to move the feeds about is simply foolish. If deer feeding were stopped it is dubious whether the corpses of starved deer lying about the glens in springtime would be regarded with the equanimity of the old days. It might be used as a weapon, despite the flawed logic, for berating lairds for under-shooting again. The benefits of winter feeding for the performance of deer themselves, particularly for antler development, are scientifically not quantified, but stalkers' evidence suggests it is significant. We feed stags at Borrobol in several locations: some thirty royals (twelve-pointers), or more, walk the winter hills nowadays whereas before feeding started a royal was a rarity you stopped to admire. I have yet to meet a stalker who doubted the efficacy of feeding – given the objectives mentioned above. Deer farmers have demonstrated how dramatically physical size can be improved with feeding and the largest farmed deer swell to about twice the dimensions of their heather-dwelling compatriots. If this were insufficient proof of the growth potential of red deer, the American elk or Scandinavian wapiti, vastly heavier than our own hill-dwarves, makes the point irrefutably.

It is not always logic that has governed the way Scottish deer have been managed. Feeding in winter is an example. Many people have done it without altering their stag cull to get the benefits. If more stags are pulling through the winter, more are available to shoot. The logic of this has not invariably been followed. If a better class of stag is treading the turf as a result of better sustenance, then a better class of stag can be shot. The whole level of the herd will have climbed a notch. On the other hand this cannot be taken too far. The disingenuous claim of the greens, that a Scottish landscape reclothed in trees will leave unaltered the finances and employment on estates, is not thought through. A higher class of stag in a woodland setting would equate to the form of stalking which is over-supplied elsewhere. What has been mentioned to me by my American clients as the charm of Scottish open-hill stalking is that one stalk is followed by another; the day is a repetition of climaxes.

The type of stag selected for shooting – the cull beast – has also been put under the microscope by scientists. Some have argued that a stag is as good as its feeding, that a disreputable six-pointer one year can, given the feeding, become a royal the next. So it can. However, the application of this to stag cull policies is tenuous. The purpose in selecting for shooting the old stags past their prime, and inferior stags because they clutter up the ground and will breed their like, remains broadly correct. For the argument that any stag can become respectable is irrelevant unless that stag can get access to the feeding which will enable him to achieve it. The fact remains that the good stag has consolidated his position and stature by utilizing the feeding available. The genes which enabled him to out-perform the average stags have a chance of being invested in his offspring. Leaving him to sire his like is a solid approach. Constantly taking out the under-performers will not eliminate their gene pool from the forest, but it will over time improve the average of the survivors. The question of genetics remains one of the great unknowns regarding red deer, and is relevant in helping decide stag culling policies. The foremost scientist of red deer in Britain, Dr Tim Clutton-Brock of Cambridge University, is presently looking at heritability amongst stags; no empirical conclusions have yet been reached. Having already shown that stag performances is closely influenced by environmental factors during the stag's young life, condition of the mother, what sex calf she reared previously etc., he is reluctant to concede at this stage a strong position for genetic hereditability. Deer managers will track with interest the progress of his researches to discover the proportion of a stag's performance that is hereditary.

Stag quality aside, many lairds have looked at their deer culling the wrong way round, or in a way that is weak in logic. They say: we have so many deer on the ground so our cull is this. Or: we have always shot so many stags, we must continue doing so to sustain the capital value. By looking at the deer from the habitat outwards a different philosophy may prevail. For instance: there is little point in shooting a large number of stags if they are all concentrated into the last three weeks of the season. Few stalking tenants want to shoot more than three beasts a day, or dozens in the week. Two or three a day usually suffices. The last few deer are carcasses in the larder, but they become less sporting as the season progresses, their senses muffled from the rut. When the sex drive dominates all, they can be approached more easily and dispatched without great sporting satisfaction; stalking then can become something of an indignity. The owner of such a forest might instead take the view that the back-end stags are not of great rental value therefore a lower cull might be more appropriate, and more lettable. A lower population of hinds might serve the purpose just as well. In other words environmental benefits could accrue without enormous loss of venison income. The classic answer to this is: what about capital values? Traditionally they have attached to numbers of stags shot. I question whether this is still so. An obvious proof is that many deer forests sold today are selling to charities or conservation bodies with no interest in stalking. These buyers are looking at the potential for regenerating trees not deer, or protecting landscape. Income considerations need not so keenly apply. Sportsmen too are changing their requirements. Remoteness, physical beauty and scenic grandeur are now part and parcel of an estate's assets.

Speedier and more flexible communications, like helicopters, have made practical quick visits to places hitherto protected by their inaccessibility. A deer forest in Sutherland sold a few years ago for an enormous price apparently because of its unusual physical splendour, or certainly on a cost-basis which had little to do with the modest deer cull. The owner was a keen sportsmen but sporting returns did not dominate in his pool of requirements. This point of view has arrived on the scene to stay. In many ways it is refreshing. The traditional policy of keeping up the stag cull for the sake of capital values has an application still, and will continue to do so until stalking as a sport fades away, but fashions are changing fast. In the future an estate which can boast a lowish cull, taken sporadically over a longer season, in a setting enhanced by environmental diversity and differing habitats, may prove the new ideal. Stalking will remain the core for the time being, but the intensity of a last-minute cull, amidst stags pursuing hinds, may lose value. Already many estates have cut short their cull, and are taking stags earlier in the season for superior venison and better sport. In these places the height of the rut is a time when deer are left to themselves, in the fever of their pro-creative urge. This seems right, and a disinclination to shoot 'run' beasts shows refinement creeping into the sporting market-place too.

Many different influences will determine how the management of deer forests will evolve. The certainty is that overall deer numbers will be lowered and not allowed to rise again. Counts and culls will be watched closely. It is likely that deer forests will become more venison-driven than in the past. Higher health and hygiene standards for deer larders demanded by the EC will punish the pockets of deer forest owners, but they will also help dispel the myth that venison is rough stuff, brought to the market-place in a haphazard way. The Safeways initiative in marketing has already started doing this. Shooting earlier stags will marry neatly with the objective of producing better meat. The fewer 'run' stags that enter the market-place the higher the quality of venison reaching the consumer. The need to lower deer numbers will entail shooting not only old stags and hinds but younger, tenderer ones. Culls of mixed age classes will help the venison trade and prevent deer populations from struc-tural disarray. The spread-out culling will help game-dealers to provide fresh meat over longer periods. Stalking stags in July and August is in many ways the finest time to do it. The weather is pleasant, the days long, the light good, and the stags often in grand parties, travelling the range and reaping the benefits of the herbage at its richest. Stags have not reached their heaviest body-weight by early summer, but otherwise all that is missing is the antler in hardened form. The liabilities of operating commer-cially in remote, wild places, which mainly show up in the costs of carcass collection (around 20 per cent of game-dealer operating costs), can be offset by skilful marketing of the venison image. Reared on fertilizer-free open range the animal has enjoyed an unencumbered life without the disturbing cycle of dips, anaesthetics and medications. The meat is healthy and rich in flavour. The proportion of wild venison exported has to date been around 80 per cent. There is plenty of room to lower that figure and increase the home uptake. At the inauguration of the Association of Deer Management Groups it was revealed that the home market traditionally mopped up the lowest-grade venison while the best went abroad: low domestic consumption of venison is presumably connected to this.

Another feature which will influence deer forests is the make-up of ownership. So much reverts in the end to this matter of who owns land and for what purpose. The reasons that institutions are rapidly gobbling up Highland estates in preference to private proprietors are manifold. Economics underlies them all. If private deer forest owners paid no taxes they might be able to compete with charities bidding for deer ground. A pipe-dream? Not quite. The charismatic owner of the spacious forest of Letterewe in Wester Ross, Paul van Vlissingen, told a recent assembly of landowners, in-between exhortations to them to argue their case more convincingly, that in his home country, Holland, relief from taxes had been achieved. Over many years a comprehensively-inclusive union of landowners had besieged a succession of socialist governments with proof that private ownership of land was good for the Dutch state. Finally the Dutch government had succumbed. Capital taxes on any estate-owner who could prove that he had managed the ground in a responsible conservationist manner have been cancelled. It is unnecessary to spell out to anyone fiscally literate what this could mean for deer forests. It is equally unnecessary to explain to anyone politically literate that this concession has as much chance of sneaking down our own corridors of power as a snowball in hell! The fact is that capital taxation deters landowners from treating their estates in Scotland to long-term management agenda. The private deer forest buyer in the 1990s is typically a person who has made enough money to buy the supreme sporting luxury; assembling the cash takes time. He is unlikely to be under forty. At death he knows the estate will probably have to go, or it will be split and chopped up to raise money for taxes. This discourages the long view which is appropriate to land management, and which applies to other forms of land-holding such as farmland which do benefit from tax relief.

Purchases by charities, government institutions, and national institutions, are part of a long-term realignment. In a way it is logical that some of the most emotionally-contested land-ownership in Britain reverts to the state. State ownership defuses, in theory, the quarrels and historic bitterness. As it happens, in Britain ownership by corporations is occurring nationwide, and in the 1990s the large farmland purchases on best arable ground have also been made by, sometimes between, institutions. The consistent failures of British governments to develop a policy for the countryside, agricultural production and forestry has brought about the corporatization of the land-holder, a result no socialist ever imagined resulting from the absence of central government objectives. Corporate landowners have cash reserves to weather the storms. In the Highlands they are buying, and have bought, ground for ideological purposes not financial ones. Campaigns to paint traditional land-ownership in the worst possible light – the RSPB's pogrom against Highland gamekeepers was particularly vindictive – enable them to raise the money to replace those they criticize. It is in the nature of charities, set up to protect something, to need a steady supply of fresh, critically-threatened subjects. Crises are the life-blood of fund-raising initiatives, and if they are not there they must be manufactured. An outsider to the Highland scene witnessing the furore over Mar Lodge, and the demands by conservation bodies that government match its funds pound for pound in an £11 million buy-out, would have deduced that this piece of inhospitable ground, most of which lies above 2500 feet, was one of the great natural treasures of all time, truly on a scale of ecological magnitude with the Brazilian rain forest to which it was compared.

The fact that institutional ownership is vested in the name of a majority, or a group, provides some form of protection from the popular press. Conversely institutions, particularly eco-friendly ones, need to be more sensitive about their image than private people. Frequently welcoming the public has been developed as a trade-off against land uses which are open to criticism as being unneighbourly or experimental. Thus institutional owners have been able to draw visitor-pressure away from commercially-run properties when deer stalking is going on, a service for which estates can be grateful. The presence of institutions as lairds has had a mix of consequences. One of the definite ones is that it has led to a diminution of ground run primarily for sporting uses.

The land market has been specially accessible to institutions in the early 1990s because of the collapse in deer forest values. Over winter 1992–3 around 10 per cent of all deer forest range was formally for sale and nearly fifty estates languished on the market simultaneously. A backlog of properties was waiting in the wings for estate agents' books to clear and prices to revive. Deer forest values which had plummeted from £100–200 an acre in the feverish late 1980s, fell to levels as low as £20 an acre. One idea currently being circulated is that deer forest rates follow the precedent set by rates on salmon fishings. In a surprise move in the late 1980s these were abolished for properly constituted river boards in Scotland so that the monies could be spent on conservation and protection measures. There is talk amongst deer management groups of the same applying to deer forest rates.

Change would have to be statutory. The concession would be more logical and politically defensible if, in future, the environmental benefits could be proved. No assessment of the rating relief's success was ever asked for regarding fisheries, perhaps because of the costs of monitoring it.

There are two ways in which the management of deer forests is due to change permanently. One is culling policy in the light of the findings of science, and the other is the incorporation of the deer cull into a policy for management of the hills in the wider, ecological sense. Progress towards this more developed outlook has been ragged, and often the views of the different interest groups have become polarized. The reason for this is that the high-profile drive against deer numbers, simplistically presented by the media and worked to a froth of indignation, fell victim to its own propaganda, and eventually deployed blatant misinformation to advance its case. Journalists were prone to going straight to one of the fringe anti-deer advocates and taking their cue as given, without further ado. As time cools the temperature of debate the principal areas of misinformation become clearer. The first is to do with the timing of the population explosion. The big increases were between 1965 and 1975; deer numbers advanced more slowly after that. The reason was simple: sheep stocks fell by 20 per cent between 1966 and 1978, approximately over the same decade. The biomass shifted from sheep to deer. Respectable newspapers ran shock-horror stories about red deer being physically squeezed by their degraded habitat. There was never any evidence for this. Calving rates change with population pressure, as shown, but declining bodily condition and increased mortality due to population density never occurred. Talk of antler size going down was speculative, unscientific, and almost certainly the reverse of the truth. The evidence of aerial photographs mentioned earlier, showing that

Scotland's vegetation profile is changing never established the causes; sheep effects were never separated out from those of deer or climate. Two of the key scientists relevant to the deer range debate, Des Thompson and Tim Clutton-Brock, agree that one of the critical areas for further scientific research is to separate out deer and sheep effects on vegetation, using models with differing ratios of each animal and different types of vegetation. Because of this last confusion the deer debate has been conducted in a sort of weird vacuum, often ceasing to have meaning to those on the ground presently managing the deer and sheep. Deer population reduction has seldom been talked of in the only sensible way – in conjunction with reduction in sheep numbers; assuming, that is, that there is a case for lower grazing pressure in the first place. Reducing one and not the other will merely lead to increased fertility, bodily condition and productivity in the other.

The desirable density of grazing animals will differ from area to area. One of the benefits of this baptism by fire of deer managers at the hands of propagandists is that recognition is now universal, amongst the bodies and individuals that count, that deer management should be addressed on an area by area basis. An obvious illustration: at present over half the wild cull is from the Grampians, a small part of deer range geographically. In other parts of the Highlands numbers probably could never have built up to support such a cull. The mineral-deficient steep west Highland slopes, dropping sharply into the sea are a quite different management proposition to the colder eastern Highlands with their heather-covered rounded mountains. The carrying capacity of hill ground varies widely.

The unresolved question remains the future of those areas selected for the natural regeneration of woodland. The Cairngorms Working Party's report has arrogantly and foolishly recommended itself as a blueprint for land management elsewhere. It should not be. It is a report which puts the Caledonian Forest regeneration above all else, and if it became a prototype management plan we would live to regret it. The report differs fundamentally in outlook from the findings of the other Highlands working party, commissioned at the same time, that on Loch Lomond. The Loch Lomond Working Party report is unpublished at the time of writing, but it makes detailed recommendations on the control of visitor numbers, an area circuited in the Cairngorms. The bare truth is that if woodland in the Cairngorms or anywhere else is to be regenerated on deer range the deer numbers need reducing to a minimum. Where natural regeneration of broad-leaf trees is sought, numbers have to be suppressed even lower than for conifers. People have argued about how many deer per square kilometre will permit trees to cast their seed and regrow. The answer, as Creag Meagaidh showed, is very few. Deer would have to be virtually eliminated to achieve the aims desired. The obvious practical answer, espoused by all except the extremists, is to fence; to fence and then to cull out the proportionate number of deer that had been using the fenced-off area. This way a mixed land-use is maintained while habitat becomes more diverse. This way too the landowner remains in place, or has a chance to do so, one reason possibly that it does not prevail in the report.

We have come of age as far as looking at the desired ecology for individual areas. The hard choices about options for change under the Caledonian canopy have yet to be made. Although the estates owned by conservation bodies in other parts of the Highlands will opt for habitat improvements of various sorts as a priority, the main body of open-hill ground in the Highlands is not directly under present threat. On this area the science-guided management of open-hill red deer will, given the *status quo,* continue and improve. A key research area in this connection is the demographic factor in stag dispersal. This has long been the subject for speculation by stalkers, who have tended to believe that some stags, the ones they refer to as 'travelling stags', will go long distances in the rut to integrate with fresh genetic pools of females. Great distances have already been logged for individual stags. This subject would require investigation into how far stags disperse, and what relation this migration has to hind densities on their wintering grounds, and also on the grounds to which they journey.

Scottish Natural Heritage (SNH) will play a major part in the development of deer use in the Highlands. Magnus Magnusson is the present chairman and he also chaired the Cairngorms Working Party. There are clear signs in the 'one step forwards and one back' approach of the final Cairngorms document that he had considerable difficulty accommodating some wilder opinion in the ranks. The ultra-green bubble has yet to burst in Scotland and until it does SNH will remain uneasy – and landowners will remain uneasy about SNH. In the annual lecture given in 1992 to the Natural Environment Research Council Magnus Magnusson referred to this strain with a confession that SNH might have been 'guilty of sectoralism'. In its founding charter SNH was made responsible for sustainable land-uses, a definition including human employment. He went on to talk about 'paying the true costs of utilization of our natural resources and our environment'. This has specific application for deer forests through the management agreements reached by SNH with landowners on Sites of Special Scientific Interest, known as SSSIs. In the early days payments were made to landowners to persuade them to abstain from developments thought unsuitable. This system had obvious defects, the most publicly aired one being that no-one could be sure if certain landowners were putting up fanciful proposals in order to get the payments. A refinement of the idea was created in the Peatland Management Scheme specifically for Caithness and Sutherland, a proactive concept in which acceptable management is rewarded. Under this a five-year management contract was signed in which the landowner agreed a management policy. He could reserve for himself those activities he needed to continue, typically stalking and carcass removal, in return for not entering into new management plans. The areas for closer discussion involved sensitive subjects such as heather-burning. This is not disallowed under the management agreements, but landowners must be specific about which areas they want to burn and why. A modest payment, calculated on an acreage basis, is then made annually for the duration of the contract. Personally, on Borrobol, I have found my Peatland Management Scheme works well, and I have been happy with the way agreement was reached and implementation of it has been monitored. In the future SNH expects to move towards management agreements in return for active conservation undertakings. However, progress towards agreements like the Peatland Management Scheme were not straightforward and initially, when policies were being formulated, there was talk of landowners being paid to radically reduce deer numbers for habitat regeneration and to curtail sporting use in the area. It was not understood at this point how critical cull numbers of deer were for estate finances and for stalker employment. The revised system in its limited area appears, in most cases, to work well, operating as it does under the voluntary principle. The most obvious trap into which it could fall is becoming translated into a rationalization of an ideal target for red deer populations, determined by a government agency. What criteria should be used? Who would decide them? Such a move would open the way for maximum dissent. The RDC shrink from having to stipulate such a blunt figure. Many commentators on the deer scene, including the leading deer scientists, see the possibility of this development as a disaster.

The more radical organizations would prefer to see SNH empowered to compel landowners into management agreements on SSSIs and punish transgressors. This would instantly heighten the tension between landowners and their regulators, make membership of the SNH boards itself a political issue, and dismantle at a stroke the incentives for owning Highland property. Voices within SNH are not at one about this, although public disagreements have been contained. The prospect of more power is appealing to some. Longer heads view the emasculation of the private landowner, going cap in hand to the door of the local SNH office for permission to do this and that, with horror. Very soon the land would decline in financial and social value and employment would plummet. The route to full public and institutional ownership would be swift – and very expensive. Civil servants would effectively run, manage, and populate communities which had partially lived off the estate system. The longer term effects might come sooner into play than expected. These would revolve around economic and unecomonic uses of land.

It is hard to argue that purist conservation prescriptions for deer range do not involve reduced employment and reduced financial self-sufficiency. The removal of most of the sheep and deer living on deer range would destroy shepherds' jobs and stalkers' jobs, and severely hurt local business; nothing serious has been proposed to compensate. A further point which has never been addressed is that whole wildlife balances would change, most sharply in predator populations. It is for example a fact, though uncomfortable for wildlife sentimentalists, that in extensive areas where sheep have been cleared the numbers of eagles have declined, so have those of foxes. The likelihood is that

146

in the wake of the sporting lairds other commercial interests would enter the picture, the first arrival being forestry. This nation, along with most others, is simply not affluent enough to transfer into cold storage a large part of its land-mass for high-minded conservation notions uncontaminated with serious proposals for productive output. If the sporting estate was abolished, or made redundant by the stringency of restrictions, it is naive to imagine that the way would be clear for unopposed greening of the hills. Sooner rather than later, after the reserves of timber from Russia are stripped out, as is precipitately happening now, the economics of timber-growing, even in this temperate climate, will jump forwards. The deer forest lairds are a last bastion of mixed land-use as a principle. This has been perceived by a wide number of people. Frank Fraser Darling, a tough outdoors-man who walked the mountains in bare feet in sharp stylistic contradistinction to the ilk of present-day ecologists who hail him as their mentor, saw the exteme dangers of nation-alization in the Highlands. In many places in Scotland, particularly the islands, local people who had relished inveighing against the laird have been horrified by the out-landish representatives, and notions, of the institutions by whom he has been replaced. The RDC and most of those within SNH fear the disappearance of the private owner of land; it is to be hoped that the politicians of the future will heed them.

Attention should be directed to refining the present system. As Tim Clutton-Brock has always been at pains to point out, the answer to the question of the right number of deer depends on the ends sought from the deer resource. The aim of yielding the maximum amount of venison would allow for a larger population than the requirements of a forest which was designed for letting stag stalking. Managing a deer forest for venison produc-tion is unlikely to be an option in the contemporary context. Venison prices are still too low to justify it; high stocking of deer runs contrary to deer management group policies and present ideas about the preservation of good vegetation health – on high ground it can damage delicate plant communities – and it will lower the quality of the stags and depress the breeding performance of hinds. Most deer forest owners run their ground for a mix of reasons which include venison production, but few regard it as a priority. The better course, and one which all the mainstream interests in Scotland's red deer are already embarked on, is to reduce hind populations, and some-times also stag populations, to a size which lightens their effect on vegetation. This will improve stag sizes and stature, and improve the image and desirability of Scottish stalking. Cull numbers should be worked out by local management groups, listening hard to what the RDC rec-ommends in that area. If the condition of the vegetation on the hill is to be used as a marker for deciding culls, along with deer population factors, as Des Thompson suggests, stalkers need training in it. It is remarkable when living on a piece of ground what changes can occur without arousing comment. This is because focus is easily lost at close range. Outside help and opinion must be sought from time to time, and deer forest employees and owners, must shrug off the old-fashioned attitude of privacy and secrecy. This is what got them into trouble with deer numbers in the first place. Habitat measurement should be adopted as a routine practice, and the devel-opment of tracking in new places, and over-pressurized ground, sharply watched for. The science of deer counting needs improving. If the RDC believes its infra-red methods are efficacious it should properly research and publish the proof. The RDC and deer scientists have found that cross-checking generally reveals a habitual under-count, but the degree of under-counting is unknown. Anyone who has been involved in deer counting will know the difficulties of getting it right. Red deer, once named 'the dun tenants of the waste', have an extraordinary way of melting into the ground.

The answer to stalking's troubles is that the sport needs a revitalization. Young people need to be involved. It is a quite remarkable thing how many individuals of both sexes, given the opportunity to stalk deer, surprise themselves with their keen response. I recall someone who came to Borrobol accompanied by a girl who was determined to stalk. He was to go along for the walk. When she got her first beast he was astonished at the radiance on her face and the lift in her spirits. She was veritably pumped up. The day continued in relaxed vein, passing deer here and there, until we came on the next stalkable proposition. The stalker signalled him forward, pointed at the animal, and he felled it. It seemed so much the natural thing to do he never questioned it, or remembered that he had set out as an observer. Without ever intending to take up the rifle he had become, in that moment, 'keen as mustard' in the gamekeeper's phrase. A year does not pass without him sallying forth again, now a stalking man to his braces. I have several times taken people stalking for their first beast, and always the result is the same. Expectations are disproved by the experience, prior apprehensions forgotten. The enthusiasm for stalking is growing in Britain, but open-hill stalking for reds is not getting the lion's share of the new interest. I know a Texan who uses the sporting possibilities on his ranch to rehabilitate youngsters from troubled backgrounds who have turned troublemakers themselves. The programme has proved an excellent way of giving them new purpose. He told me a curious story about a young tough guy who went out on the ranch to shoot a deer. When he accomplished this he went up to the body with a look of disbelief on his face. Then he fell on it crying, not in pity or remorse, but because it was his first possession. Make of it what you will.

Some stalkers and hunters only shoot deer. They travel the world looking only for members of this one family. Perhaps it is a matter of habituation. But I feel like that too. Wherever in the world I have seen them, the deer species have for some unaccountable reason interested me most. I have never shot them abroad, but I have always watched them closely. As several of the people I talked to in writing this book said, the red deer is the most valuable animal we have. European man has had a working relationship with red deer for as long as any other wild animal. In Scotland it has become a national symbol. We must care for it well.

# *Index*

151